# Managing
## PERFORMANCE
# Measurement Data
## in Health Care

JOINT COMMISSION RESOURCES

## Joint Commission Resources Mission

The mission of Joint Commission Resources is to continuously improve the safety and quality of care in the United States and in the international community through the provision of education and consultation services and international accreditation.

Joint Commission Resources educational programs and publications support, but are separate from, the accreditation activities of the Joint Commission. Attendees at Joint Commission Resources educational programs and purchasers of Joint Commission Resources publications receive no special consideration or treatment in, or confidential information about, the accreditation process.

For more information about Joint Commission Resources, please visit our Web site, at *www.jcrinc.com*. For more information about the Joint Commission on Accreditation of Healthcare Organizations, please visit *www.jcaho.org*.

# CONTENTS

# FOREWORD

There are a plethora of publications available which are designed to educate the interested reader about the use of statistical analytic techniques relevant for use in health care settings. Similarly, there are many books available pertaining to performance improvement approaches as applied to health care. Among the missing, however, is a publication that blends both topics and provides guidance on transforming data into usable, actionable information. *Managing Performance Measurement Data in Health Care* is designed to do just that.

Within health care today, the measurement of performance is a given. Organizations devote significant resources to the very act of measurement, but too often, measurement itself is the sole goal. Lacking is a blueprint by which organizational leaders can assess their information needs, plan for appropriate data collection and analysis, and reap the rewards of investments in measurement by using data to make more judicious decisions.

This publication presents a user-friendly approach— including several case studies and numerous examples— to understanding data management and selecting and using tools derived from statistical process control to assess trends and patterns in health care data and, finally, describes the Joint Commission's current approach to using these tools within the context of the ORYX initiative.

Jerod M. Loeb, PhD
Vice President, Research and Performance Measurement
Joint Commission on Accreditation of Healthcare
Organizations

# INTRODUCTION

Today's health care environment forces the issue of providing high-quality care at the lowest possible cost. This means organizations must build processes into their systems that are both clinically effective and financially efficient. To accomplish this, processes must be continually monitored, reviewed, and revised (as necessary). Where to start is often the primary stumbling block of most facilities: Which processes should we monitor? How do we know whether a process is performing optimally? If we make changes to a process, how do we know whether the process has improved? What, if any, impact have changes to one process had on related processes?

Most health care organizations have some sort of quality management or performance improvement program in place to improve their care delivery and, whenever possible, decrease their costs. Data play an integral role in all improvement activities, providing the basis for objective, well-prioritized decision making. However, although many organizations diligently collect data, they don't always know how to analyze data (find out what data really mean), present data (display findings in a usable format for improvement activities), or use data (find performance trends and patterns that can indicate opportunities for improvement) effectively. This book is designed to help readers with each of these steps.

Chapter 1 provides an overview of the data management process and explains how it fits with performance improvement programs. Chapter 2 discusses how the data management process can be used to improve performance. Chapter 3 focuses on data collection techniques to simplify the process and preparatory steps to ensure that the data being collected are valid, reliable, and useful. Performance improvement tools and systems thinking tools are presented in Chapter 4, which demonstrates how various methods can be used together to present data results and facilitate analysis. Chapter 5 explains how to use statistics to analyze various types of data for performance evaluation. Finally, the case studies in Chapter 6 furnish real-life examples from different health care settings in which data management techniques have been applied effectively.

A case study exercise is presented in Appendix A to help readers test their understanding of concepts explained in the text. Based on information about an actual restraint reduction program in a long term care organization, this self-study exercise provides a review and examples of key concepts, along with questions for the reader to answer. Appendix B includes sample questions about performance measurement that may be asked during surveys. Additional resources for data management and statistical process control, and their use in performance improvement activities, are provided at the end of the book.

## ORYX Applications

A recent example of a large-scale application of statistical process control methods in performance measurement is the Joint Commission's ORYX™ Initiative, which integrates performance measurement into the accreditation process. At the same time, accredited organizations have an opportunity to measure and use their performance data for internal performance improvement as well as external demonstration of health care accountability.

The Joint Commission first began using ORYX performance measurement data in the survey process in January 2000. A health care organization's selected performance measures are printed in the Joint Commission–produced ORYX Pre-Survey Report™, along with graphical displays of the measurement data and any statistically significant findings. The surveyor uses this information as a reference tool during the on-site survey.

An organization's selected performance measures are analyzed in monthly increments. The Joint Commission performs statistical analysis after each quarterly data transmission deadline. The listed performance measurement systems (often referred to as "vendors") are required to provide feedback to their respective clients by the time they transmit ORYX data to the Joint Commission. Ideally, both the health care organization and the Joint Commission should have access to the same data each quarter on the organization's selected ORYX measures.

Data management is an important component in analyzing and using ORYX data. To help readers apply information to their data management processes in this area, sidebars with the heading "ORYX Tip" appear under relevant topics. The sidebars also point out potential trouble spots to avoid when collecting and analyzing ORYX data. As an additional aid, Appendix B lists Joint Commission standards that relate to the management of ORYX data and how surveyors may address them during an on-site survey.

## Terminology

This book is intended to help a variety of health care organizations address their data management plans. Because each setting has its own terminology, the text uses the following terms generically throughout:

- *Patient*—Anyone receiving care, treatment, or services from an organization, including residents (long term care), individuals being served (behavioral health care), members (networks and preferred provider organizations), and clients (home care).

- *Staff*—Those who work within a health care organization, including administrative staff (such as receptionists and information technology personnel), clinical and nonclinical care staff (such as physicians, nurses, psychologists, anesthesiologists, physical therapists, laboratory technicians, and dietitians), and support staff (such as maintenance, housekeeping, and volunteer staff).

- *Family*—Those who play a significant role in the patient's life and form a social support system for him or her (may include people who are not legally related to the patient).

- *Medical record*—Clinical record, chart, health history, and so forth.

- *Care*—Clinical and nonclinical interventions (care, treatment, or services).

- *Health care organization*—Any facility delivering care, treatment, or services, including ambulatory care centers, assisted living facilities, behavioral health organizations (residential and nonresidential), home care agencies, hospitals, and long term care institutions.

Setting-specific examples in this book use the appropriate terminology.

No one book can have all the answers, especially on a topic as wide ranging as health care data management. However, *Managing Performance Measurement Data in Health Care* provides a solid foundation on which organizations can build, as well as techniques and examples that can be adapted to all types of settings.

## Acknowledgements

This publication would not have been possible without the contributions of Judy Homa-Lowry, RN, MS, CPHQ, faculty and intermittent consultant for Joint Commission Resources, Oakbrook Terrace, Illinois; Janet Houser, PhD, Principal Consultant, Abacus Systems Consulting, Loveland, Colorado; Kwan Y. Lee, PhD, SM, Project Director, Division of Research, Joint Commission on Accreditation of

Healthcare Organizations, Oakbrook Terrace, Illinois; and Christine McGreevey, RN, MS, Associate Project Director, Division of Research, Joint Commission on Accreditation of Healthcare Organizations, Oakbrook Terrace, Illinois, each of whom dedicated much time and energy to writing the chapters in this book.

We are also grateful to the following, whose organizations served as case studies: Chris Lind, RN, Nurse Manager of Health Services, and Jon Zeipen, MSW, Coordinator of Quality Measurement, Hazelden Center City Recovery Services, Center City, Minnesota; Stephanie Morahan, Administrator, Parker Jewish Institute for Health Care and Rehabilitation, New Hyde Park, New York; Yosef Dlugacz, PhD, Senior Vice President for Quality Management, and Lori Stier, RN, EdD, Administrative Director for Quality Management, North Shore–Long Island Jewish Health System, New York; Elaine Vieira, RN, CCRN, BS, Manager for Performance Improvement and Corporate Compliance, South County Hospital, Wakefield, Rhode Island; and Linda Lesher, LPN, Continuous Quality Improvement/Infection Control Coordinator, and Jennifer Mowery, BSW, Director of Social Services, Susquehanna Lutheran Village, Millersburg, Pennsylvania.

We would also like to thank the internal staff; surveyors Ceile Fontaine, Jackie DuPlantis, and David Perrott; and the following, who reviewed the manuscript and provided valuable feedback: Bev Cunningham, MSN, RN, Regional Director, Clinical Effectiveness, Mercy Health Partners, Toledo, Ohio; Rebecca Kerr, PPS/JCAHO Coordinator, Good Samaritan Village–Long Term Care, Hastings, Nebraska; Christina Knoderer, BA, Director of Quality/Risk Management, HealthSouth Rehabilitation Hospital, Fayetteville, Arkansas; and Regina McClurg, MSW, CSW, Director, Professional and Organizational Development, Gerontology Network, Grand Rapids, Michigan. And finally, we owe tremendous gratitude to Karen Steib for shaping and honing this publication into a user-friendly resource.

# CHAPTER 1: Data Management: The Foundation of Performance Improvement

Judy Homa-Lowry, RN, MS, CPHQ
Faculty and Intermittent Consultant
Joint Commission Resources
Oakbrook Terrace, Illinois

## Defining Data Management

In order to evaluate the performance of a health care system and, more importantly, the care that system provides to individuals, it is necessary to have information. Because the health care system in the United States is so complex, organizations require information derived from multiple data sources to evaluate their performance. Performance measures are tools that assist organizations in evaluating their systems and collected data to maintain and sustain improvement. There are multiple references in this text to the terms *system* and *process*. The following definitions from the Joint Commission's *Lexikon* are provided as a foundation for the use of these terms[1]:

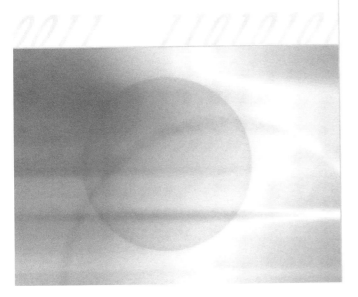

- A *system* is a network of interdependent components, such as emergency medical services, that work together to try to accomplish the aim of the system.

- A *process* is an interrelated series of activities, actions, events, and mechanisms or steps, as in the hospital admission process, that transforms inputs into outputs for a particular beneficiary or customer.

### Clarifying Data Needs

The first challenge for many health care organizations has been to identify the data necessary for an effective performance improvement program. Many resources are expended in collecting data. In many organizations, there are a multitude of data, but the data are not always converted into useful information for the intended audience. The data should provide insight about the effectiveness of systems and operations in an organization.

Performance improvement methods can help organizations identify how effectively their key systems are operating. It is necessary to determine what systems and processes are in place in order to identify the performance measures needed to evaluate how effectively these systems are functioning. All organizations have developed performance measures, but these may not be linked to all of the internal systems. The performance measures may have been developed in response to regulatory requirements or to something of interest. If they are not constructed properly, the value of the data from these measures may be limited.

One way to identify an organization's systems and its corresponding data needs is to consider three categories of performance measures: the strategic/business plan, regulatory requirements, and contractual obligations. These are interrelated; none of them is independent of the others. The rationale for selecting these three categories is to provide a comprehensive approach to evaluate an organization's critical systems. In some organizations, these systems are evaluated separately. Performance measures to evaluate the corresponding processes and outcomes to each of these categories need to be developed. Information needs to be available to link and evaluate the effectiveness of each of the organization's key systems.

Some organizations capture the same data (or parts of them) using their balanced scorecards, dashboards, organizational matrixes, or some other method. The key to whatever tool is being used is that data provide information to the functioning of important systems and processes.

This is the beginning of the data management process. The organization needs to determine what data are necessary to evaluate its performance. This should include quality control data. Identifying data that provide insight as to how well the organization is meeting the objectives of its strategic/business plan, regulatory requirements, and contractual obligations is one way to continue to build an effective data management/performance improvement program.

*Collecting Data*

Prior to determining what data are to be collected, it is helpful for an organization to perform a data inventory (also discussed in Chapter 3, page 40). This inventory is intended to identify all of the data/information an organization is currently collecting and receiving from outside resources. Performing this type of exercise allows the organization to evaluate whether it needs to continue with all current data collection activities.

The first step in the process is to identify all of the committees, teams, and task forces that exist. It is extremely helpful if the organization is familiar with the purpose for each of these groups. This may sound fairly simplistic, but some organizations continue to add teams and committees without evaluating the need for them in their current infrastructure. Existing teams and committees may be able to address new issues. The need for existing teams and committees may have changed, and some may be combined or eliminated. These teams and committees, as well as departments, typically generate the need for data. This is why it is important to determine the purpose and the responsibilities of the committees/teams/departments needing the data.

Once all teams and committees have been identified, the next step is to ascertain all of the data required to support their existence. Examples of data collected in a data inventory would include all indicators, performance measures, external data reports, logs, journals, and so on. The objective of this process is to establish a central location for all of the data currently being collected and purchased for the organization. If people are not aware that data are currently being collected or purchased and they need that data, they will collect them. This often results in duplication of effort and different results if the data are not collected in a consistent manner. Even though the concept seems obvious, individuals need to be taught how to perform data collection. In many organizations, staff are asked to collect and analyze data without formal training. It is well worth the investment to train them in the process of data collection.

Once the data inventory is performed, the next step is to determine whether the data being collected are being duplicated by other teams, committees, or departments. Duplication may occur by either manual or computerized data collection or abstraction. Some individuals and/or departments collect these data multiple times. For example, how many departments are collecting patient satisfaction data? A decision should be made as to who will be responsible for collecting the data and how the data will be shared with the appropriate departments.

One of the most obvious questions to raise after completing a data inventory is to ask whether people are using the data. This is true for the data they are collecting as well as for the data they are receiving. If the data are not required in any of the categories previously discussed, staff should be told to stop collecting them. This may seem obvious, but most individuals are not familiar enough with the organizationwide performance improvement program and specific standards to determine whether there is a need for continued data collection.

In order to collect meaningful data, time must be spent finding or, if necessary, developing performance measures that are meaningful for the organization. Issues to address in the development of performance measures are how to identify measures, determine their purpose, define them, and test them for validity and reliability (each of these issues must be addressed according to Joint Commission standards). Organizations also need to determine the appropriate sample size, ensure consistency among individuals in collecting the data, periodically audit the data collection activities, and detect trends and patterns of performance that should be evaluated. Once this has been completed, data collection efforts can be initiated.

Most measures should have a numerator and denominator in order to calculate rates. (See Chapter 5, page 98, for more information.) Performance measures need to be comprehensive enough to address the processes and outcomes of organizational and departmental systems. In terms of accreditation, one way to accomplish this is to review the information required in the Joint Commission's closed medical record review for the type of organization that will be surveyed. Health Care Financing Administration (HCFA) medical record requirements, National Committee for Quality Assurance (NCQA) medical record requirements, state licensing requirements, mental health code requirements, and so on should also be reviewed. These items provide a good foundation for identifying performance measures within an organization. The list of measures needs to be defined. If it is not, individual reviewers may add their own definitions as to what information needs to be present in order to be in compliance, which leads to inconsistency in data collection and results. The best way to define measures is to refer to the standards and the organization's policies and procedures, which define its systems and processes. An organization's compliance with these policies and procedures is determined by monitoring the results of performance measures.

To determine whether a measure is valid, the data must be reliable. To determine whether the data are reliable, data elements must be well defined. The organization should determine whether there are clear and consistent data definitions present for all the data elements. This can be accomplished by collecting samples of data for each measure/indicator. The reason for using clear, consistent data definitions and sampling the results for performance measures is to determine whether the measures will produce reliable and valid information. It is important that data elements have the same meaning for everyone. Many times, data elements are not well defined. This can result in data collection that does not provide the information desired to evaluate performance. It may then become necessary to repeat data collection until the same results are produced for the measure consistently over time and the results truly identify the process being studied. Rework is not a positive force for encouraging personnel to be part of the performance improvement process.

An appropriate sample of the data to be collected should be determined. This is done to create a baseline for measurement. Sampling can also be used to evaluate large populations where it is unrealistic to review each item, patient, medical record, and so on. There are many different sampling techniques. Even if an organization is small and there are not many deviations from expected outcomes, there are specific sampling techniques to address such samples. (Sampling techniques are addressed in Chapter 3, pages 50–52.) Once the data have been defined and collected, the analysis can begin.

## Analyzing Data

Data can come from external or internal sources. External data, many of which are financial, mortality, morbidity, and patient satisfaction data, are obtained from an outside vendor. With the exception of patient satisfaction data, external health care data are primarily obtained from claims data. There are also several databases for medical specialties, as well as special projects done by external health care agencies, universities, hospital organizations, and insurers, to name a few. The second data source is that collected internally.

Typically, data obtained from external vendors have already had some preliminary analysis done. For example, the data may be severity or risk adjusted. If this is the case, it is important for the user to understand the approach the vendor has used to do this. Understanding the vendor's methodology assists in answering questions concerning the integrity of the data. It is also helpful if the methodology has been peer reviewed. This provides the organization with the opportunity to evaluate the strengths and weaknesses of the data in measuring and evaluating what they are intended to measure. Some vendors' methodologies do a better job of measuring outcomes than others. The differences in outcomes may be attributed to different types of diagnosis-related groups (DRGs), risk- and/or severity-adjustment models, age of the population, and payer. (An excellent resource for reviewing these issues and existing severity- and risk-adjustment methods and products is *Risk Adjustment for Measuring Healthcare Outcomes* by Lisa Iezzoni, MD.[2])

Some other questions also should be addressed when using external data. Were the data from administrative or claims sources? Were the data abstracted from medical records? Are only MEDPAR (Medicare) data used from all payers? How many organizations are in the database? Do the organizations in the database represent all U.S. regions for comparative purposes? How are the norms and benchmarks calculated? How often is the database updated?

The data collected in the organization should be analyzed using statistical and nonstatistical tools. Employees need to be trained in the use of these tools. The training should include the use of data from their departments and committees. Many training programs only include the definitions and concepts concerning the use of performance improvement tools. If staff are able to see their own organization's data in the training programs, there are more favorable results in terms of using the statistical and nonstatistical tools. Individuals within the organization should be identified for performing data analysis. Certain disciplines have had more extensive training in the use of these tools because of their background. Laboratory professionals, social workers, and psychologists are just a few examples of professionals who have been trained in statistical techniques and who can provide assistance in analyzing data. The type of organization and the staff employed will determine how data analysis should be performed. (Data analysis is discussed in more detail in Chapter 4.)

There should be a mechanism in place to periodically evaluate performance improvement data for validity and reliability. This can be done by having individuals skilled in data collection and analysis periodically sample data collected by other professionals and evaluate the integrity. In some organizations, performance improvement professionals conduct these audits. Other organizations have committees that evaluate the data. Auditing the integrity of performance data on a regular basis can avoid expensive rework in the data analysis and management component of the performance improvement program.

## Using Data and Information

The primary use of data and information in a performance improvement program is to prioritize areas for improvement. With decreasing reimbursement and a reduction of available resources, organizations need to have a way to prioritize their opportunities for improvement and the resources that will be needed. Using data and information provides a more objective approach to setting these priorities. The use of data also provides organizations with a quantitative method for monitoring their performance improvement efforts.

Data need to be presented in a format that is specific to the intended user. If there are a great deal of data to report and they are not organized for the user, they will not be used. An example of this would be a number of narrative reports containing data that are not trended or do not highlight any trends or patterns. This makes it difficult for the decision maker to understand the issues contained in the reports. (Chapter 5 discusses ways of presenting data results.)

Data should be shared with the individuals responsible for addressing the issues identified in the report. In many organizations, performance data are collected, analyzed, and reported to leadership. Even if a problem involves a specific unit, many times the data are not reported by or shared with that unit. Organizations should share data from quality control activities, infection control activities, environment of care monitoring, and human resources with all appropriate departments. Unit managers, as an example, need to know that their equipment is in good working order. There should be a mechanism whereby the unit manager receives a report from individuals responsible for monitoring activities on his or her unit. When the unit manager is held accountable for activities on the unit or in the department, that manager needs to receive all appropriate data. The type of health care organization and its performance measures will determine the data flow needed to ensure that everyone receives the data needed.

Another problem can occur if the data are not complete enough for the user to make a decision. An example of this would be a group that receives data about length of stay (LOS) without any corresponding utilization data. For this reason, most organizations have converted from narrative performance reports to dashboards or report cards, which include multiple measures and allow data results to be trended over time. These tools also provide an opportunity to evaluate the measures' impact on various processes in the organization simultaneously.

Performance measures should be trended over time to see whether there are significant changes, trends, or patterns. The performance of the entire organization and its departments should be monitored to assist the organization in determining whether an issue was identified throughout the organization or is present in only one department. There have been situations where an organizationwide process has been completely changed when only one department was responsible for the poor performance. If the issues are identified and resolved in one department, there may not be a need to change the system for the entire organization. This approach can result in cost savings and can also assist in evaluating how the organizational priorities for improvement are communicated to various departments.

All of the organization's performance measures should be included in one report presenting measure data that are trended over time. This approach allows the user to evaluate to what the change in the trend or pattern may be attributed. It also does not give a false sense that because everything in one area is fine, this is true for the entire system. An example to illustrate this approach would be to consider the data used for three reports to the board required by Joint Commission standards for many health care organizations. The first report comprises human resources data; the second looks at the environment of care; and the third addresses performance improvement. The environment of care and human resources reports state that everything is fine in the organization. However, the performance improvement report notes that there have been equipment-related employee injuries. In addition, there is no education program scheduled to address the proper use of equipment. This example illustrates the need to evaluate all data at the same time to avoid a false sense that all systems and processes are working well together and are integrated. This approach also should enhance an interdisciplinary approach to performance improvement. Whatever type of organization is involved, all reports containing data should be analyzed simultaneously to identify issues and evaluate the effectiveness of the organization's systems and processes.

Financial data may not routinely be used in performance improvement programs. Yet there is a need to begin to report financial measures and their relationship to other performance measures. This is especially true when examining the cost of corrective actions to address opportunities for improvement and their effectiveness.

## Defining Performance Improvement

The term *performance improvement* has been used frequently in this chapter. The definition of performance improvement according to the Joint Commission is "the continuous study and adaptation of a health care organization's functions and processes to increase the probability of achieving desired outcomes and to better meet the needs of patients and other users of services."[1]

This terminology has been evolving since 1980, when the Joint Commission first specifically addressed quality, with its quality assurance standards. Because there was concern that quality could not be "assured," the term was changed to *quality assessment* in the mid-1980s. It was then recognized that simply assessing quality did not mandate efforts to improve quality, so there was a need to revise the terminology again. Around 1990, the term *quality improvement* was initiated. However, there were so many debates about the definition of *quality*, it was decided to use the term *performance improvement* because performance can be defined and improved.

Defining performance for all aspects of health care organizations has been a challenge and has caused organizations to invest numerous resources in determining performance standards. The Joint Commission has recommended the following ways to set performance goals/standards in its management of information standards:

- Identifying specific issues in medical records;

- Noting trends and patterns in the organization;

- Referencing the scientific literature; and

- Comparing data.

## The Relationship Between Data Management and Performance Improvement

With the continuing evolution of the performance improvement standards, there has been an increased emphasis on the need to evaluate established systems and processes. Even if a process is changed or modified, it needs to be monitored for effectiveness according to Joint Commission leadership and performance improvement standards. Examples would be policies and procedures for sample medication, restraint use, and health care screening and prevention.

Such evaluations cannot be completed without data. A major emphasis in the performance improvement standards is to collect data and transform them into information. Specific standards address the need to collect data about various organizational processes and patient care outcomes. Organizations use statistical process tools to evaluate performance. As previously mentioned, the information management standards also require the use of data and information to evaluate performance.

Organizations are encouraged to collect and use baseline data, which help in determining whether there is an important issue to address. An evidence-based decision can be made to determine whether an issue is significant enough to warrant further investigation. For example, if someone in the organization states that part of a process "is hardly ever done," a baseline sample can be taken to determine whether this issue is worth pursuing. The process can help in eliminating unnecessary data collection efforts. Baseline data also can be used to determine organizational priorities and as a comparison to demonstrate successful performance improvement efforts.

## Goals of Data Management

In organizing the data management process, it is helpful to have established goals. Some specific goals that should be established may include the following:

- Data should be simple and understandable. When data are complex or the intended audience is unsure of the message being sent with the data, the data will most likely not be used. The presentation of the data also should be simple and understandable.

- The data should be concise and precise. As previously discussed, the data should be specific in terms of what is being measured. There should be no questions concerning data accuracy.

- Users should generate the data. It is important that the users of the data be involved in the process of collecting, analyzing, and using them. Not including individuals in the data management process for their areas of responsibility can have a negative effect on how the information is used.

- The data should help make decisions, improvements, and actions. This reinforces the need to have a purpose established for gathering data. If the purpose or planning phase of a project is not established first, data management efforts will not produce the desired outcomes. These outcomes include the ability to make data-driven decisions, improvements, and actions.

- Consumers are becoming increasingly more interested in health care delivery. Data concerning the quality of care being given at various health care facilities are being made available to the public. The release of such data and an increase in the amount of information available to consumers through the media and the Internet has increased the expectations and the demand for high-quality health care services.

### Patient-Centered Outcomes

According to Emad Rizak, MD, identifying patterns in process and health care services using patient-centered outcomes can assist organizations in targeting the following areas[3]:

- Improving services and care;

- Establishing benchmarks for provider performance and setting therapeutic goals;

- Tracking and comparing performance over time, including linking information systems that merge medical and drug information with individual and provider profiles in order to analyze program effectiveness;

- Developing evidence-based clinical practice guidelines in order to improve diagnosis, treatment, and individual monitoring;

- Establishing clinical "centers of excellence"*;

- Assessing new and existing technologies;

- Monitoring an organization's quality improvement efforts, as well as provider and individual compliance with clinical guidelines;

- Helping individuals and purchasers select high-quality providers; and

- Educating individuals about self-care and creating communication that influences provider and individual behavior.

*Health Status.* The focus of many, though not all, performance improvement programs is to evaluate the health status of patients. The focus of data management activities over the years has evaluated whether patients improved based on clinical interventions. Many performance improvement activities mandated for hospitals by the Joint Commission have focused on the following reviews: surgical interventions, medication therapy, special and diagnostic procedures, blood usage, rehabilitation, and infection control activities. Networks focus on immunization status and breast cancer screening. Some activities specific to behavioral health are establishing the presence of a behavioral health disorder requiring treatment; determining the clinically appropriate level of care; and providing specialized treatment services for substance abuse, mental health, and dual diagnosis.

Many organizations purchase or review reports from their corporate offices or clinical associations that show the number of deaths and complications—according to specific DRGs or body systems—within a health care system or region, or nationwide. These reports enable organizations to compare their patient care outcomes with those of similar organizations to identify opportunities for improvement. Many of the reports also illustrate the number and type of resources that were required to treat patients. This information is helpful in studying trends and patterns of patient care and the changes seen in the management of patients. The comparative reports and the corresponding information are helpful to many organizations in establishing clinical pathways.

The evaluation of a patient's health status may be accomplished in a number of different ways. Blood pressure readings and/or laboratory tests can help in the assessment of functioning for physiological status. For physical status, this may be determined by activities of daily living. Cognitive skill and effective interaction may assess mental or psychological status. Social status may be assessed by the

---

*center of excellence* A tertiary care facility that has established a reputation for superior quality in one or more areas. Its reputation tends to draw patients from extended geographical areas, thereby lowering the cost of providing care through economies of scale.

ability to engage in work or school activities. Other health-related quality-of-life areas include pain, energy, sleep, and sex.[4]

Two purposes can be achieved by evaluating health status: People in need of services may be identified before a catastrophic event occurs, and health status can serve as an outcome measure for care or treatment received.[4]

*Functionality*. The patient's ability to function after an intervention is also a measure of patient care outcomes. As previously mentioned, national studies have been in progress to study the health outcomes of patients. These include initiatives by the Joint Commission, Carl H. Slater from the University of Texas, HealthPartners, Aetna U.S. Healthcare, the Veterans Administration, and the Health Plan Employer Data and Information Set (HEDIS). Some organizations that disseminate outcomes research include the Agency for Health Care Research and Quality, Association for Health Services Research, National Library of Medicine, Stratis Health and the Health Outcomes Institute, and Medical Outcomes Trust.

*Wellness*. The ultimate goal of prevention efforts is wellness. Data concerning prevention activities are constantly collected and monitored. Screening and prevention activities are designed to improve individual care outcomes. Screening activities include tests for colorectal cancer, high cholesterol, prostrate cancer, and cervical cancer. Examples of prevention activities are smoking cessation, nutritional counseling, and stress reduction. Data are collected on the participation in such programs through many health care plans. In addition, immunization rates and first-trimester prenatal visits are monitored. The link between these activities and outcomes is studied by many managed care plans. Poor performance in this area may cause a potential purchaser of a health care plan to consider other plans that have more positive outcomes.

*Perceptions of Care/Satisfaction*. According to Peter R. Kongstvedt, MD, service quality measures the timeliness, responsiveness, and courtesy with which managed care organizations serve their members.[4] These same issues tend be measured in all health care organizations. Trends and patterns from this type of information are used to identify performance improvement opportunities. Some of the common concerns raised in terms of individual satisfaction are whether the care provided was correct and appropriate. The caregiver may have failed to explain what was being done, neglected to explain how and when to take prescriptions at home, or made the patient wait a long time for an appointment.[4]

It is worth noting that individual satisfaction questionnaires tend to have a return rate of less than 35%. Patients who are very pleased or displeased with their service are usually those who complete surveys. An organization needs to look at its number of respondents. If the response rate is less than 35%, what types of things are being done to increase the response rate or sample size? (A response rate of less than 20% will likely lack any credible statistics of the whole population.[5]) Even though it is not realistic, surveying all patients would provide valuable feedback concerning perceptions of the quality of care being provided.

It is also extremely important to monitor patient/family complaints. These complaints can provide insight into potential problems with organizational processes. This is especially true in light of the national concerns regarding corporate compliance issues.

*Other Outcomes*

As mentioned at the beginning of this chapter, the health care delivery system is very complex; as a result, multiple data sources are needed to evaluate organizations' numerous systems and processes. The following are some examples of important nonclinical issues that should be measured through a performance improvement program.

*Organization Stability and Growth.* As mentioned previously, the business/strategic plan should also be measured as part of the performance improvement program. This usually has not been—and still is not—included as part of many organizations' improvement activities.

The criteria for health care organizations applying for the Malcolm Baldrige National Quality Award suggest that organizations have a strategy development process in place that includes the following five areas[6]:

- Target customers, market requirements (including price, customer, and market expectations), and new opportunities;

- The competitive environment;

- Risks (financial, market, technological, and societal);

- Organization capabilities, human resources, technology, research and development, and business processes to seek new opportunities and/or to prepare for key new requirements; and

- Supplier capabilities. (For a more detailed list of criteria, see Table 4–2, page 7)

The next part of the process is to examine how this strategy would be deployed in the organization. This includes translating the information into action plans, including critical requirements, and tracking performance relative to the plans.

*Operational Issues.* The strategic planning process should include how the organization intends to put the strategic plan into operation. This includes strategy and action plans, human resources plans, and the performance projection[6]:

- The strategy and action plans should describe how resources are deployed to ensure alignment of goals and actions. Important differences between short- and long-term goals should be addressed.

- The human resources plans should include changes in work design and the organization to improve knowledge and sharing, flexibility, innovation, and rapid response. Employee education, deployment, and training need to be addressed. Changes in compensation, recognition, recruitment, and benefits also should be part of the process.

- The performance projection should be time related. Comparisons are done on a periodic basis with competitors and industry benchmarks. Estimates and assumptions should be included in this process.

It is worth mentioning again that the organization should review all of its policies and procedures to ensure that they reflect actual operations. If they do not, they should be eliminated or modified, or new policies should be developed. This is necessary to begin the measurement of processes. There is no point in constructing control charts that reflect the consistency of processes if there is no organization-wide agreement on what the process is for a particular operation.

*Reputation/Community Standing.* These outcomes center on the organization's ability to address societal responsibilities. They include how the organization addresses the current and potential impact of its facilities, services, and operations in the community. The operations and their impact on regulatory, legal, and ethical requirements also need to be addressed. The organization should anticipate public concerns, assess possible actions that may involve the community, and address them in a proactive manner. There needs to be an emphasis on the organization and its employees, and their role in strengthening their relationship with the community.[6]

*Employee Satisfaction.* One of the issues to consider in evaluating employee satisfaction is whether, through performance improvement activities, something will be done to address the issues identified by employees. It is important to consider this when surveying employee satisfaction so the process does not end with negative connotations. The following factors from the Baldrige award criteria can be taken into account when evaluating employee satisfaction: effective employee or grievance resolution, safety, employee views of management, employee deployment and career opportunities, employee preparation for changes in technology or work organization, work environment, workload, cooperation and teamwork, recognition, benefits, job security, communications, compensation, equality of opportunity, and capability to provide required services to customers.[6] Additional measures of satisfaction include absenteeism, employee turnover, turnover rate for customer-contract employees, grievances, strikes, and workers' compensation.

*Financial Issues.* As mentioned earlier, financial indicators need to be part of the performance improvement process. Typically, financial measures have included LOS, disenrollment rates, charges, and reimbursement issues. These measures should also include return on investment, margin rates, operating profit rates, profitability, liquidity, and financial activity measures; and may include market share, business growth, and new markets entered.[6] Most organizations do not include this information as part of their performance improvement process, although such information should be combined with clinical outcome measures. Balanced scorecards or dashboards can be used to accomplish this.

The need to conduct cost-effectiveness and cost–benefit analyses for potential corrective actions for performance improvement activities needs to be expanded in health care organizations. In some performance improvement programs, corrective actions are suggested without any financial calculations as to the cost and benefit to the organization.

*Compliance with External Standards and Regulations.* The need to comply with external standards and regulations is an important part of a performance improvement program; however, it is unfortunate when the primary existence of such a program is tied to the goal of a good external survey. The need for a performance improvement program supercedes the need for accreditation or licensure, which is to ensure that the organization is meeting minimal standards for individual care.

One factor that is particularly frustrating when attempting to meet all external regulatory requirements is the inconsistency of requirements from various regulators. This may initiate the need for multiple processes. At times, it appears that one process may be in direct conflict with another.

Organizations should assign an individual or a group of individuals to monitor the changes in all external regulatory standards on an ongoing basis. These monitoring activities need to be done in a timely manner. A mechanism to address how the organization will address changes in the standards also needs to be present. This will help to ensure consistency. The "rule" is that if two regulatory agencies are mandating practice, the stricter one is enforced. This philosophy can cause potential conflicts in an organization, primarily centered on the potential to affect reimbursement. The question is whether, if a process is consistently applied and is not required by the payer, the organization may lose significant dollars in operating costs. These are issues that need to be addressed on an ongoing basis with leadership and concerns that should be shared with the appropriate regulatory bodies.

Organizations also need to address supplemental recommendations from external surveys in a timely manner. At times, these are missed or not addressed until shortly before the survey.

Compliance with all regulatory standards can be a challenge. Providing data definitions of the areas to be addressed is a good place to start. For example, how does the organization define an adverse drug reaction or a significant medication error? The greater challenge occurs when the regulatory body states that something must be measured but does not define it in the standards. Two problems may occur. The first is that the organization does not define how it will comply with the standard. The second is that the organization defines how it will address the standard but does not follow its own guidelines.

If organizations set performance measures and continually monitor their systems and processes according to the standards, survey preparation will be ongoing. This will also help to ensure that these processes become part of the organization's operations instead of just temporary measures put in place for external surveys.

# Requirements for Successful Data Management

## Leadership

Leaders need to be involved in an organization's data management processes. In many organizations, the performance improvement priorities tend to be determined by external regulatory requirements or from information from departments, committees, teams, and task forces. The leadership needs to have data and information to assist them in setting organizational priorities for improvement. This process will help leaders track and review priorities on an ongoing basis to determine whether they need to be revised.

Leadership also should be involved in determining the organization's data management education needs. The organization should periodically perform a data needs assessment to determine that its data needs are continually being met. This will assist employees and leaders in using data.

*Leading by Asking Questions.* Leaders can be involved in successfully resolving issues if they learn to ask the right questions. According to Russell Ackoff, "A question is a further abstraction from a problem; it is an exercise from which the reasons for wanting to solve it and its context are not revealed. A question is a problem completely out of context."[7]

The point is that once data are presented, the appropriate questions must be raised to elicit solutions or identify additional problems. Many people have been involved in meetings when the data presented led to more issues than solutions. This may be due to the questions being raised instead of the data being presented. The reasons for wanting to answer a question determine what constitutes the right answer. The principal difference between excellent and ordinary organizational diagnosticians does not lie in the differences of their diagnoses from the same information, but in the questions they ask to obtain additional relevant information.[7]

*Evidence-Based Decision Making.* Decisions based on data, or quantitative information, are more objective than those that are not. Organizations are able to further analyze a problem when data are available, thus allowing the organization to determine the scope and severity of issues. This is also helpful in setting organizational priorities. Dashboards, report cards, external comparative data reports, and scientific data are all tools that can be used to assist in data-based decision making. They also facilitate the simultaneous monitoring of multiple performance measures over time.

*Knowledge.* The recommended skills for using data appropriately include a knowledge of research methods (databases using empirical data, risk- and severity-adjusted data), basic statistics, and computer skills (for more complex data management activities). In many organizations, if research is going to be done to study a specific issue, professionals with this type of training are present within the organization.

Most organizations teach employees who are responsible for performance improvement activities basic statistics. They may also invite consultants to provide training or make provisions for employees to receive training outside the organization. In some organizations, performance improvement professionals may be the individuals responsible for using statistical tools to analyze performance improvement data.

Most organizations have computers available to assist staff with collecting and analyzing performance improvement data. There are software packages that can perform statistical analysis, report findings, and display data graphically. The statistical analysis can also be calculated manually. Again, computer courses may be provided within the organization, or employees may receive training from an outside source. Basic computer skills such as data entry, analysis, and formatting are important to support the data management program.

### Organization Resources

The organization needs to have adequate resources to perform data management activities. Staffing should be determined. Will one department or committee be responsible for all monitoring and data-related activities? Will the performance improvement department support the medical staff's data management needs? Will department heads be responsible for the data management activities in their departments? What is the budget for performance improvement and data management activities in the organization? What factors are considered in the budget? What kind of technology is available to support performance improvement and data management activities?

These questions need to be addressed in order to calculate a budget for providing adequate resources to support an effective data management and performance improvement program. One way to construct this budget is to review all of the committees, teams, and task forces and determine the need for their continued existence. Eliminating unnecessary meetings is one way to redirect human resources into the performance improvement program.

The data inventory discussed earlier may indicate which performance measures can be eliminated. This provides the opportunity to reallocate financial resources into performance improvement. The remaining performance measures can be categorized into measures for the strategic/business plan, regulatory requirements, and contractual obligations. By eliminating data collection and meetings that do not add value to the organization's data management and performance improvement programs, it is possible to reallocate these resources to address current deficiencies without increasing the budget.

## Summary

The benefit of using data wisely is the ability to identify and address variations in patient care and organizational performance. These variations may be due to patients, organizational processes, practitioners, environmental factors, or random variations. Using data will assist the organization in identifying and analyzing these factors in order to improve patient and organizational outcomes.

## References

1. Joint Commission: *Lexikon*, 2nd ed. Oakbrook Terrace, IL, 1998.

2. Iezzoni LI: *Risk Adjustment for Measuring Healthcare Outcomes*. Chicago: Health Administration Press, 1997.

3. American College of Physician Executives: *Clinical Resource and Quality Management*. Tampa, FL: American College of Physician Executives, 1999.

4. Kongstvedt PR: *Essentials of Managed Care*. Gaithersburg, MD: Aspen Publishers, 1997.

5. Fowler FJ: *Survey Research Methods*. Thousand Oaks, CA: Sage Publications, 1993.

6. U.S. Department of Commerce: *The Malcolm Baldrige National Quality Award*. Gaithersburg, MD: National Institute of Standards and Technology, 1997.

7. Ackoff RL: *The Democratic Corporation*. New York: Oxford University Press, 1994.

CHAPTER 2:

# Using the Data Management Process to Improve Performance

Janet Houser, PhD
Principal Consultant
Abacus Systems Consulting
Loveland, Colorado

Performance improvement is dependent on the management of data. Data are key to effective improvements made by organizations, but only after those data have been identified accurately, measured reliably, analyzed appropriately, and transformed into information. Once data have been analyzed, the results can be used in a variety of ways in the performance improvement process.

The primary uses of organizational data are for planning, screening, diagnosing, and accessing.[1] Data used for planning answer the question, "Are we achieving our strategic vision?" Planning data support activities such as forecasting efforts, designing programs, and setting priorities. Data used for screening help determine opportunities for improvement by pointing to processes that are out of control and whether variation is due to special or common causes. Data used for diagnosis support the

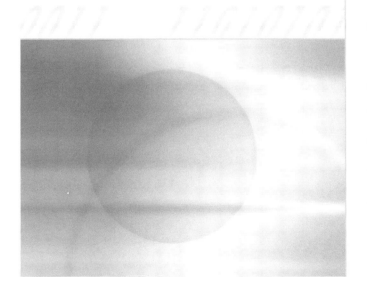

search for causes of problems. Diagnostic data help teams focus interventions on the most common causes of performance variation. Monitoring data are used to ensure that stable processes stay that way. Data are used to access the effectiveness of improvement interventions and the progress of teams.

Data also are used in more subtle ways in the performance improvement process. Teams are most effective when their membership has been determined based on data about team member performance, team leader competence, and facilitator skills. Data are used to express the outcomes expected from teamwork and to measure team progress. Data about resource needs and justification for the application of resources are critical if teams are to generate a return on the resources consumed. Finally, data are used to ensure that gains made by improvement teams are maintained.

Virtually every step of the performance improvement process is grounded in the information that is generated through data collection and analysis. Without it, organizations may draw faulty conclusions, invest resources unwisely, and fail to maintain improvements.

Both qualitative and quantitative data are used in the performance improvement process. As noted in Chapter 1, health care is delivered in a human context, operating within complex systems. Perceptions of effectiveness and satisfaction are often as important as actual physical results in the patient's determination of an overall desirable outcome. A focus on quality of life and functional outcomes requires that both qualitative and quantitative information be gathered, analyzed, and used effectively. Reliable measurement, accurate collection, and appropriate analysis of both types of data become critical skills for the organization that wishes to effectively improve performance.

Reliable, valid measurement is key to the capture of relevant, useful data. Measurement does not have to be burdensome, but it does need to reflect performance in an accurate way. *Reliability* refers to the consistency of measurement given a specific measurement tool. A measurement is reliable if it consistently produces results in which the only variability is due to the process, not to measurement error. A valid measure reflects the process or performance it is intended to measure. For example, a measure of depression should reflect the condition of depression and not anxiety or a sleep disorder. Chapter 3 (pages 52–54) provides various methods for validating data quality.

In addition, measures should be sensitive and specific. A measure is sensitive if it is able to detect subtle changes in the underlying process or performance—in other words, if it doesn't produce a false sense that the process is performing correctly. A measure is specific if it measures only the underlying process or performance, and not artifacts or confounders. Simply put, it should not produce a false sense that the process is performing correctly or incorrectly. Effective measures possess both sensitivity and specificity for a given process.

Finally, data will not be collected consistently if the collection process is overly troublesome or not well defined. Automated sources reduce the burden of data collection and retrieval. User-friendly forms and standard measurement tools support efficiency in the collection of accurate, complete data.

The selection of performance measures should be done systematically. Many aspects of measurement are considered in determining an effective set of measures. The purpose of the measure, the dimensions of performance being measured, and the ultimate strategic goals of the organization must all be considered when choosing effective measures. Chapter 1 gives detailed information about different types of performance measures.

## The Leadership Role in Performance Improvement

It is the responsibility of the leaders of an organization to ensure that data are measured effectively and transformed into information, then used reasonably and thoughtfully to achieve improvements. They should determine how data are used to guide performance improvement efforts.

Leaders set the tone for performance improvement, identify the organizational approach, determine how data are used, and ensure that performance improvement efforts are communicated effectively. They are the critical link between the concept of performance improvement and its implementation through employee participation.[2] As such, leadership must be focused on team development, as well as on the organizationwide performance improvement process.

One of the most important functions of leadership relative to performance improvement is the identification of priorities for performance improvement efforts. This is not a capricious process. The Healthcare Advisory Board reported that the appropriate identification of priorities, coupled with an organizationwide focus on a single performance priority, was the only strategy that resulted in "quantum leap" improvements for an organization.[3] It makes sense then that the organization's leaders must give thoughtful consideration to the criteria used for prioritizing improvement opportunities.

## Setting Priorities

Leaders must systematically identify those critical areas where outstanding performance is required if the organization is to accomplish its mission. Otherwise, improvement efforts create outcomes that don't contribute much to the central issues of the organization.[4] A general approach is shown in Figure 2–1 (page 22) and begins with a list of all of the issues, problems, concerns, or potential improvement projects. These should be generated based on qualitative and quantitative data. Requiring that supporting data be provided with a request for project consideration ensures that the project is justified. In addition, requiring supporting data restricts the number of issues to be considered to those truly worthy of consideration and avoids wasted discussion time.

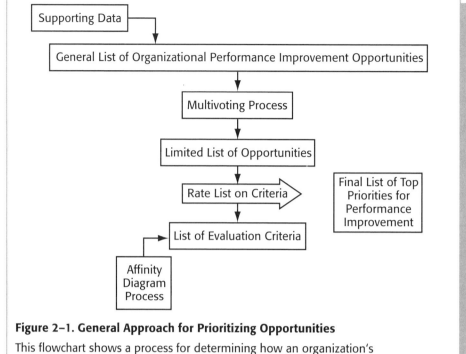

**Figure 2–1. General Approach for Prioritizing Opportunities**
This flowchart shows a process for determining how an organization's opportunities for improvement can be prioritized. This includes gathering a list of problems, using a prioritization matrix and multivoting to narrow the list, applying evaluative criteria to each problem, and making a final list using a weighted prioritization matrix.

### Multivoting and Prioritization Matrix

One helpful tool to manage the priority-setting process is multivoting, which is used to systematically achieve consensus on a condensed list of the most important items. Each participant is allocated a fixed number of votes that can be applied to the list of issues. The votes may be allocated in any way the individuals wish—for example, they may allocate five votes to one issue they feel is extremely important, or one vote to each of five issues they feel are equally important. The votes are tallied for each issue, and the top issues are retained according to a predetermined limit. The process may need to be repeated as needed to achieve a manageable list.

A note of caution is warranted about the use of multivoting. Because of the distribution of votes, an issue may receive a high rating when only one or two participants find it important. A critical last step in multivoting is to ask the group, "Does this list make sense for us?" The group must achieve consensus on the results before the list is finalized.

A second mechanism for limiting the list of issues is the prioritization matrix. A prioritization matrix is a general tool used to prioritize opportunities for improvement or proposed solutions.[5] It is a form of convergent thinking used to reduce the number of considered opportunities to a realistic, manageable size. Its purpose is a structured, data-driven approach to determine the improvement opportunities most likely to be successful and to affect the overall organization in a meaningful way. The matrix has three general components: the issues or topics being considered, the criteria used to prioritize the issues, and the rating scores for each issue.

## Evaluation Criteria

The second step in prioritizing is to brainstorm a list of criteria against which to evaluate the list of issues. An efficient way to establish a succinct list is to use an affinity diagram. An affinity diagram is a structured approach to develop a short list of items quickly. It combines ideas into similar groups, resulting in a manageable number of topics. Like a prioritization matrix, it is a form of convergent thinking that uses a systematic approach to group ideas logically into a smaller set of categories.[5]

The affinity diagram process begins with brainstorming all of the potential criteria that can be used to evaluate performance issues. Each participant does this individually, in silence, writing each idea on a sticky note. After all participants have recorded their ideas, each is asked to put the notes on a flip chart, explaining the meaning of each idea. After all ideas are posted, the group is asked to silently group the notes into logical categories. The categories are named and subsequently become the criteria for evaluation of issues.

Some of the criteria commonly used by health care organizations are as follows:

- Impact on the customer;

- Need to improve;

- Urgency of the improvement need;

- Relationship to the organization's strategic plan;

- Frequency of occurrence;

- Probability of success;

- Financial impact;

- Leadership interest;

- Effect on patient outcomes;

- Physician satisfaction;

- Support of the organization's mission; and

- Regulatory requirements.

It is worth noting that the probability of success for a performance improvement endeavor is heavily dependent on leadership's support and skill in managing the performance improvement process. Thus, it makes sense for the evaluation criteria to include leadership commitment to the project, the availability of a competent team leader and facilitator, the ability to engage medical staff (if appropriate), and the release of employees to work on the project. These, more than any other factors, may influence the number of projects that can be empowered at any given time.

Once the criteria for evaluating issues have been identified, each issue is rated on each criterion. A prioritization matrix is helpful to manage this process (Figure 2–2, below). Each participant rates each issue against the criteria, using a predetermined numerical rating scale. This does not need to be a quiet process. In fact, the strength of the prioritization matrix is not as a paper tool, but as a focus for leadership discussion. The scores are then tallied. This may be done a variety of ways. The individual scores of each participant may simply be added, or the scores may be averaged. The scores are then added across all criteria, and a single final score is assigned to each issue. The top issues are considered against the final criteria: Does this list make sense?

### Weighted Prioritization Matrix

Often, not all evaluation criteria are of equal weight. For example, alliance with the organization's strategic plan may be more important than the frequency of occurrence. In this case, criteria may be assigned relative weights. The weights are then used as multipliers for the scores on each criterion, and these weighted scores are used for the final tally. An example of a weighted prioritization matrix and its scoring is given in Figure 2–3, page 25.

| Criteria ➡ <br><br> Issues ⬇ | Relation to Strategic Plan | Financial Impact | Positive Patient Impact | Support of Mission | Probability of Success | Total Score |
|---|---|---|---|---|---|---|
| Pain management process | 2 | 2 | 5 | 5 | 3 | 17 |
| Restraint and seclusion process | 3 | 2 | 5 | 5 | 4 | 19 |
| Network access process | 2 | 4 | 4 | 3 | 4 | 17 |
| Retention of employees | 2 | 4 | 4 | 3 | 4 | 17 |
| Cross-continuum transfer process | 4 | 5 | 5 | 4 | 4 | 22 |

Rate each issue on each of the criteria using the following scale:

0 — 1 — 2 — 3 — 4 — 5

No impact        Moderate impact        Major impact

**Figure 2–2. Simple Prioritization Matrix for a Network**

This type of diagram can be used to rate each issue or project based on an organization's evaluative criteria. The final issues to be considered are listed on the left side of the diagram, and the criteria for evaluation are listed across the top.

| Criteria and Weight ➡ Issues ⬇ | Relation to Strategic Plan (x10) | Financial Impact (x10) | Positive Patient Impact (x10) | Support of Mission (x5) | Probability of Success (x5) | Total Score |
|---|---|---|---|---|---|---|
| Pain management process | 2 | 2 | 5 | 5 | 3 | |
| | 20 | 20 | 50 | 25 | 15 | 130 |
| Restraint and seclusion process | 3 | 2 | 5 | 5 | 4 | |
| | 30 | 20 | 50 | 25 | 20 | 145 |
| Network access process | 2 | 4 | 4 | 3 | 4 | |
| | 20 | 40 | 40 | 15 | 20 | 135 |
| Retention of employees | 2 | 4 | 4 | 3 | 4 | |
| | 20 | 40 | 40 | 15 | 20 | 135 |
| Cross-continuum transfer process | 4 | 5 | 5 | 4 | 4 | |
| | 40 | 50 | 50 | 20 | 20 | 180 |

Rate each issue on each of the criteria using the following scale:

0 — 1 — 2 — 3 — 4 — 5

No impact          Moderate impact          Major impact

**Figure 2–3. Weighted Prioritization Matrix for a Network**

Using the same issues and criteria as in Figure 2–2, this matrix assigns relative weights to all criteria, reflecting their importance to the network. This makes it easier to identify the highest priorities to be addressed.

A successful prioritization process is the foundation for a successful performance improvement effort. Leaders are well advised to commit whatever time is necessary to thoughtfully and carefully consider their options. Organizational resources for performance improvement activities are necessarily limited. Their prudent application where the greatest return can be anticipated is key to ensuring that the process is efficient as well as effective. The prioritization matrix is only a tool, although it does provide a structure for intuitive decision making. In addition, its use forces all members to provide input and explain their thinking, broadening the chance that all aspects of an issue will be considered.[6] An open-minded discussion of how criteria relate to each topic also begins the process of identifying the expected outcome for each.

## Identifying Expected Results

Leaders cannot manage the process of performance improvement without clearly identifying and articulating the expected results. Quantitative and qualitative data are used to describe the outcomes expected from those charged with creating the improvement. In addition, leaders need to define all terms so that everyone

**Team Charter Statements**

*Acute Care*

Delays in the operating room determine the volumes an operating room can sustain, affect the productivity of operating room staff, and reduce patient satisfaction. Monitoring data indicate that the average surgical procedure is delayed by more than seven minutes beyond the scheduled time. Reducing this average time to less than three minutes will have an impact on volumes, revenues, productivity, patient satisfaction, and physician satisfaction.

*Delays* are defined as the difference between scheduled time for the surgical procedure and actual time the patient is transported to the operating room. Average delay is calculated only for scheduled surgical patients.

The team is to identify and recommend improvements in the preoperative process to reduce delays. This includes the preadmission process through the start of surgery, but does not include delays that occur after the surgical procedure has begun.

The team will be provided with the initial screening data. It is expected that a first progress report will be delivered to the administrative quality council within 30 days. Preliminary recommendations should be ready for pilot testing in 120 days, with final recommendations available within 6 months. All interventions should be reviewed with the administrative quality council before testing or implementation.

Team resources include paid time for team meetings, the use of a conference room, an assigned facilitator and recorder, and an assigned information management specialist. Requests for financial support should be submitted to the administrative quality council with a justification and projected return on investment.

A written progress report will be submitted to the administrative quality council monthly. The final report will include a list of suggested ongoing monitors for the improved process.

*Behavioral Health Care*

Interdisciplinary therapeutic efforts must be communicated effectively to ensure that all members of the behavioral health care team are supporting therapeutic goals. In addition, an accurate record of interventions is both an organizational and a legal requirement. A comprehensive, complete documentation process is necessary to achieve these goals. However, efficiency is key so that documentation can be completed with a minimum of effort, leaving maximum time available for interaction with clients.

Monitoring data indicate that the average therapeutic team member spends 24% of his or her time in documentation activities. Reducing this average to 15% will have an impact on productivity as well as on staff satisfaction. Indirectly, clients will benefit from the additional time available for interventions. In addition, chart audit data reflect that 11% of charts are incomplete in documentation of therapeutic interventions, and 23% are incomplete in documentation of client outcomes. Increasing the completeness of documentation will improve communication between team members while reducing legal risks and the costs of litigation.

The team is to identify and recommend improvements in the interdisciplinary therapeutic documentation process. This includes the interdisciplinary therapeutic plan, as well as documentation of activities and client outcomes.

The team will be provided with the initial screening data. It is expected that a first progress report will be delivered to the administrative quality council within 30 days. Preliminary recommendations should be ready for pilot testing in 120 days, with final recommendations available within 6 months. All interventions should be reviewed with the administrative quality council before testing or implementation.

Team resources include paid time for team meetings, the use of a conference room, an assigned facilitator and recorder, and an assigned information management specialist. Requests for financial support should be submitted to the administrative quality council with a justification and projected return on investment.

A written progress report will be submitted to the administrative quality council monthly. The final report will include a list of suggested ongoing monitors for the improved process.

involved in the improvement effort approaches the issue with a common understanding.

### Team Charter Statement

The expected results of a performance improvement effort are often articulated as a team charter or charge statement. The charter statement is a written description of expected outcomes and typically includes the following elements:

- *A statement describing the issue or problem in its current state.* This narrative includes a brief overview of the data that led to the conclusion that an issue exists.

- *An outline of the rationale for the quality effort.* This summarizes the reasons leaders agreed the issue was a priority.

- *The expected improvement.* This section includes a detailed description of the expected outcome, including any quantitative and qualitative measures which will demonstrate that the outcome has been achieved. Key terms and words are explicitly defined.

- *Scope of the team's work.* Leaders define how much work is expected from the team. It is just as important to identify what is not expected from the group. Giving a team an unmanageably large project may doom it; focusing the group's work appropriately is key to success.

- *Time frame.* Results should be expected within a specified time frame; otherwise, the team may not progress.

- *Resources.* The resources available to the team and the process for requesting them are clearly identified.

- *Reporting and communication.* Expectations for reporting on progress and communicating results are clarified.

Leaders should reflect on the finished statement to be sure it describes realistic expectations and time frames. Many times, leaders become frustrated by the slow progress of a team that doesn't meet expectations, when in reality the expectations themselves are unrealistic, poorly communicated, or misunderstood.[7] One way to ensure that expectations are clear is to rely on data to describe the problem and expected outcomes.

*Using Data to Express Outcomes.* There are two types of data for which outcomes may be expressed: sentinel events* and rate-based indicators. Sentinel events are negative, unpredictable occurrences. The expected outcome for sentinel event data is 0%, or zero tolerance. The goal is no sentinel events; the team's work is focused on making the process errorproof. On the other hand, rate-based data describe expected performance for the typical case. Expected values for rate-based data are rarely 100%; too many variables exist in an organization's delivery of care to achieve perfection.[8] Before an expected value can be set, data must be collected over a period of time to establish the mean performance of a process as it is being carried out. The leaders can express the expected results in terms of a desired rate or a range of rates. In this case, the work of the team is to improve the process itself, eliminate rework, and reduce variability in practice.

The team will use these data throughout the improvement process to identify whether the process is in control and to monitor the process over time to determine whether actions have reduced variability. An important, but often ignored, aspect of monitoring is to assess the unexpected effects of improvement efforts. In some cases, modifying one part of the process to bring it under control causes another part of the process to become more variable. For example, efforts to reduce length of stay in a network's acute care setting may result in increased visit numbers for home care or more intense care needs for residents in long term care settings. The monitoring process must be broad-based and must consider related processes as well as the process under study to make sure that improvements do not result in unintended negative results elsewhere.

The leadership discussion to articulate the expected results of the improvement effort should be thorough and specific. The goal is a mutual understanding of what is reasonable to expect from the team. This discussion also begins the process of identifying the particular resources that will be needed to achieve the expected outcomes. During this process, leaders clarify the kind of work that will be done by the team. This is the time for leaders to begin the process of identifying individuals in the organization who possess the content knowledge, process improvement skill, and commitment to achieve the results.

---

*The Joint Commission defines a sentinel event as an unexpected occurrence involving death or serious physical or psychological injury, or the risk thereof. Serious injury specifically includes loss of limb or function. The phrase "or the risk thereof" includes any process variation for which a recurrence would carry a significant chance of a serious adverse outcome.*

## Creating an Improvement Team

The exact composition of a performance improvement team is based on the knowledge, skill level, and commitment required for the effort to be successful. An improvement team should not be selected for political or personal reasons, but rather for the unique contribution each member can make to the overall results.

### Using Data to Determine Membership

Leaders can again use data to determine the appropriate team composition. Qualitative data about potential team member skills and abilities can be collected from performance evaluations, training records, and human resources files. It is useful to develop a description of the desired characteristics of the overall team. This list is used to ensure that all requirements are represented by the final team. Some of the characteristics that are typically required include the following:

- *Content knowledge.* Technical knowledge and expertise are necessary to describe the process as it is and as it is desired. Those who work within the process are in the best position to provide information about how it currently functions, and often have substantial suggestions for improvements.[9] Each aspect of process performance should be represented. For example, if the issue is to reduce the time needed to obtain an electrocardiogram in the emergency department, representatives from cardiology, the emergency department, and the order-entry system should be included. Or if the issue is to reduce the amount of time required to perform intake in an adolescent behavioral health care setting, representatives from admissions, social work, nursing, and counseling should be included, as well as individuals knowledgeable about payer requirements. Sometimes it is helpful to use a macro flowchart of the process to ensure that all subsystems are represented.[10]

- *Skill in performance improvement.* Team members use a preselected and systematic approach to address the issue. It is necessary, then, that they have knowledge and skill in both content and process. The ability or potential ability to analyze data, use performance improvement tools, contribute effectively to a group discussion, and communicate clearly are all key skills. In addition, a team leader and facilitator must be selected. While the content knowledge of the facilitator will be focused on team process, the team leader must possess skill in team management and expertise in the content area.

- *Commitment to the process and a passion for improvement.* Team members must be committed to the performance improvement process as well as possess a passion for improving the process under study. In particular, the team leader must be personally committed to creating improvements through teamwork.

- *Access to resources.* At least one team member must have the power and access to gain resources for the team. Leaders should specifically identify a team member who will have access to administrative input when needed and can request the resources needed by the team to achieve its goals.

- *Ability to empower change.* Team members should be selected for their skill and expertise, but equally important is the sphere of influence of each member. Influence is a necessary component of engendering collaborative, interdisciplinary change, where no one individual has the authority to force others to comply with recommendations. Influence is different from power; influence implies voluntary change on the part of others. Gaining a wide sphere of influence is necessary for widespread change to be achieved. For this reason, it is often desirable to be sure that the team has a balance of managers and line-level employees as members.

- *Heterogeneity of membership.* The strength of teamwork lies in the ability to gain multiple perspectives on an issue or a problem. This strength is lost if the group is homogeneous. A heterogeneous team represents different backgrounds and encourages a focus on the problem from various perspectives.[7] Each team member should supply some unique perspective or knowledge to the team as justification for his or her membership. Diversity in team membership also increases the number of potential solutions considered, which in turn increases the chances that the best solution will be chosen.

For this last reason, leaders may have a tendency to favor interdisciplinary teams over natural work groups. It is true that interdisciplinary teams are necessary to solve process problems crossing several departmental lines. But that is not to say that natural work groups cannot manage performance improvement. Indeed, natural work groups can and should apply performance improvement strategies to their own work as part of their daily activities.

Natural work groups have some basic advantages over interdisciplinary teams when it comes to solving process problems. The typical cross-functional team begins as a zero-history group—individuals who have never worked together on a project. In a natural work group, communication links are established and, although these links may not always be effective or complete, the members of the group have generally practiced expressing their feelings and thoughts to other team members. Furthermore, an interdisciplinary team loses time sorting out the hierarchy of membership and status; this has already occurred in a natural work group, which has leadership (both formal and informal) in place, allowing work to begin earlier. Finally, one of the greatest advantages of natural work groups is that they know the most about their immediate area. To receive the immediate benefits of team efforts, there is no substitute for the experience of those closest to the problem.[11]

The most carefully chosen team can fail if consideration is not given to the basic elements that make a team successful. Leaders are wise to set up a team to succeed by creating an environment for the team in which the focus is on organizational improvement, not on solving problems within the team.

*Common Characteristics of Successful Teams*

Successful teams have certain elements in common, and these elements can be measured and monitored by leadership to encourage success. The characteristics common to successful teams include

- clear goals and a written charter;

- clarity of each member's role and expertise;

- a standard process for team meetings and the team's work;

- trained and oriented team members;

- external support and recognition;

- effective leadership and facilitation;

- collaborative problem solving and decision making;

- presence of leadership with the resources to implement proposed solutions; and

- time for team meetings and assigned team work.[5,12]

Teams have been shown to create solutions that a superior to those made by individuals.[13] However, the strength of a team is not automatically achieved when a group of individuals gets together. Leaders provide the environment and guarantee the characteristics that will encourage team success, as well as provide the resources to achieve team goals.

## Resources for Improvement

Team members can achieve significant performance improvement, but not without the consumption of organizational resources. Many times, teams are empowered with an implicit expectation that they will save money and resources. In the long run, this may be true. But in the short term, performance improvement requires the allocation of resources. Much like any organizational investment, an up-front investment is required to engender long-term, stable returns.

The allocation of resources is generally interpreted as referring to financial investment. Although the investment of money is often needed to gain performance improvement, organizational resources are expended in a variety of ways to support performance improvement teams.

*Access to Information*

Teams need access to information about the process under study, relative to both its current performance and the desired performance. This information may include qualitative and quantitative data about process performance, patient/staff satisfaction with the process, steps in the process, or outcomes of the process. The team will certainly need financial information about the process.

Frequently, teams find it difficult to access the data and information they need. Obstacles to gaining access to information may include fears about confidentiality, concern that "bad" performance will come under scrutiny, or resistance to the time required for collecting and interpreting data. Team members may lack statistical analysis skills or the ability to present data in an understandable way.

The performance improvement process is heavily based on data. As such, it requires a great deal of information for analysis of the current process and for monitoring the effect of any interventions applied. The organization must ensure that the team has the resources and cooperation it needs to gain accurate, complete information if informed decisions are to be made.

### Time to Conduct Meetings

The team must have adequate time to apply the performance improvement process, evaluate data, determine interventions, and oversee improvements. This may be the most difficult resource to apply in today's hectic health care environment. Team membership is selected to minimize redundancy and maximize efficiency; it is imperative that team members are consistently in attendance. Team members paid on an hourly basis must be paid for their participation and work time with the team. All members must have plans to cover their work so they may attend meetings.

In today's geographically dispersed health care environment, organizations may need to rely on virtual teams. For health care networks in particular, it is often prohibitively expensive, in both time and money, to have consistent physical attendance of all team members at centrally located meetings. While challenging, virtual teams can be successful. They are groups of people who work together despite being separated geographically.[14] Virtual teams rely on technology, rather than travel, to get their jobs done. Teams must use whatever methods they can to keep in touch with each other and keep the momentum going. Videoconferencing, electronic real-time chat rooms, electronic bulletin boards, and shared files all may be used to maximize communication while minimizing the number of physical meetings.

Even virtual teams must have the time for an initial face-to-face start-up session. They also still need a charter, mutually understood goals, and a performance improvement process. As opposed to physical teams, though, virtual teams need training time for the technology that will enable their work, as well as for the group process. The sharing of information and solicitation of input for decisions becomes a top priority. Still, the human side of the arrangement needs attention and periodic social time, and personal contact should be planned when resources are allocated.

### Facilities and Equipment for Meetings and Communication

With settings stretched to the physical limit, adequate, consistent facilities for team meetings are often in short supply. The group needs to be able to consistently access a room that has support for team work and tools, including a marker board of some type, flip charts, writing surfaces, and accessibility.

The team also needs the resources to communicate effectively. General clerical support for the team is ideal; this applied resource allows the group to focus on solving problems rather than managing paper. Access to electronic forms of communication and streamlined communication approval processes also foster successful transmission of monitoring data and progress descriptions.

### Financial Resources to Support Team Decisions

Team decisions often involve the investment of financial resources to successfully implement an intervention. Data are used to estimate the cost of the intervention, the expected value of the intervention, and the expected return on investment. While it is unacceptable to give a team a charge to improve a process and no financial resources with which to accomplish it, it is certainly acceptable to expect the team to justify an investment of financial resources. This justification ideally links a financial return with a financial investment, but it may take other forms. Three types of financial justification data are useful in evaluating and allocating financial resources:

- *Cost–benefit analysis.* Cost–benefit analysis involves the calculation of costs and returns expected for the planned intervention. Both are expressed in monetary terms. Cost–benefit data are often expressed as a ratio, with benefits in the numerator and costs in the denominator. A figure of greater than 1.0 is desirable. Examples might be costs of a patient education program calculated against lost revenue from unplanned readmissions, or costs associated with hiring an enterostomal therapist consultant in long term care against the costs of healing a pressure ulcer.

- *Cost–effectiveness analysis.* Cost-effectiveness analysis, like cost–benefit analysis, involves estimating financial costs associated with the intervention. However, effectiveness may be measured in terms other than money. Effectiveness may include financial return, but may also describe qualitative returns, such as improved patient satisfaction or support of the organization's mission. Effectiveness includes an assessment of whether goals were achieved and is generally defined as answering the question, "Did the intervention work in a more effective way such that the investment was justified?" Evaluation of cost-effectiveness data involves judgment and intuitive conclusions about the value of the return on investment.

- *Cost–utility analysis.* Cost–utility analysis is the most complex and difficult justification to measure. Costs are measured, as with the other two methods, in monetary terms. But utility is described as the contribution to society in general, or creating a desirable state. For example, utility might be measured as a reduced number of institutionalized physically challenged children, or a decrease in teen pregnancy rates. Cost–utility is difficult to quantify and much of the data used to justify the utility of a given intervention may be qualitative, estimated, or projected.

The standards by which leadership judges the desirability of a given financial investment should be applied consistently to performance improvement projects, as they would be to any investment. Teams should know up front what data and justification are needed to request financial investment, so they can calculate and provide accurate information for leaders' decision making.

Overall, resource allocation for teams should be planned during initiation of the team's work and periodically reviewed for effectiveness. A variety of data elements are submitted to leaders to ensure that improvement efforts are focused appropriately and progressing consistently.

## Providing Support, Oversight, and Redirection

Performance improvement requires a systematic, progressive process that can involve a great deal of time, money, and organizational attention. It is imperative that leaders provide adequate support and thoughtful oversight to the team. Data are necessary for both. Review and evaluation of team performance data may require a change in direction for the team, an alteration in expected outcomes, or the allocation of additional resources.

If a charter statement has been crafted carefully, monitoring expectations for team performance data have been outlined. Leaders will have articulated the desired outcomes and outlined a reasonable timetable for change. The timetable should include periodic progress reports for leaders. These periodic reviews update leadership on team progress and serve as reminders for the team as to the desirability of the end point.[15]

Progress reports focus on gains made in the specific performance improvement project. Data identified in the charter statement should be submitted to leadership along with representations of any tools used to analyze performance. In addition, progress reports may describe progress made in team development and process. Teams go through predictable and identifiable stages as they develop, and some stages produce specific problems.[16] Attention to continuing support for team development will contribute to a favorable outcome for the team's work.

## Ensuring Systematic Implementation of Improvements

The data used for monitoring the team's progress should reflect the implementation of improvements and the results of interventions. If monitoring data have been carefully selected, they can provide information about both. To ensure that all improvements are included, a specified part of each planned intervention should be a measure of its effectiveness, a timetable for data collection and analysis, and identification of a specific individual who is responsible for collecting and presenting the data.

A useful tool for the team in establishing an intervention plan is force-field analysis. A force-field analysis is used to project the forces that will support implementation and those that will hold the improvement back. It is a qualitative analysis tool that helps a team plan interventions to ensure that the improvement is implemented with the least amount of difficulty. Using force-field analysis, a team identifies driving forces (those encouraging change) and restraining forces (those discouraging change) for a planned action. The team plans specific interventions that will maximize driving forces and minimize restraining forces. A sample force-field analysis appears in Table 2–1 (below). Measurement of data representing forces in the analysis can be used to monitor the occurrence of obstacles to be considered when evaluating team progress.

Some large projects may require staged implementation. It is a given that, in a large project, not all parts of the organization will be ready for the change at the same time. Staging an implementation uses existing resources for implementation on demonstration units to assess the impact of the approach. Staged implementation can also show enough successes that interest is sustained and additional units are more open to involvement.[15] Staged implementation may be used specifically to bypass areas of major resistance or apathy, or to avoid areas with poor leadership until the organizational change achieves the overall momentum needed for widespread adoption. Finally, staged implementation allows the team to observe both the desirable and the unexpected results of an intervention on a smaller scale, so that continuous improvement can apply to the implementation process. If a project is scaled, data (of limited scope) are available earlier to determine whether desired results are being achieved.

The team is held accountable for providing data about implementation of the improvement effort to leadership as planned. These data need to continue to be provided even after the team's work is finished to guarantee that gains are held.

**Table 2–1. A Force-Field Analysis for a Home Care Diabetes Self-Management Program**

| Driving Forces | Restraining Forces |
|---|---|
| • Illness-creating symptoms | • Misinformation about diabetes management options |
| • Family encouragement | • Lack of knowledge |
| • Physician encouragement | • Lack of resources |
| • Desire to control one's own health | • Passive attitude toward health care |
| • Past successes with self-management strategies | • Past failures with self-management strategies |
| • Past successes with teaching self-management strategies | • Lack of time for teaching and monitoring |
| | • Lack of support materials for staff |

## Ensuring Ongoing Measurement of Performance

Making an improvement requires a great deal of attention, time, and resources. Maintaining the improvement requires equal measures of attention. A variety of data are used to determine that a gain is maintained and any recurrence of the performance problem is detected and addressed quickly.[13]

For a changed process to become the standard, procedure manuals and policies must be updated with the change approach. Competence analysis of employees must include evaluation of their implementation and mastery of the changed process.

Data identified in the charter statement as expected outcomes continue to form the basis for monitoring data and analysis. Run charts and control charts are the tools of choice to monitor performance improvement and to document the results of the team's efforts (see Chapter 5, pages 87–96). One of the final tasks of the performance improvement team is to identify specific monitoring data to reflect process improvement and to identify a specific individual who will be responsible for monitoring the data.

## Summary

Data are used in virtually all stages of the performance improvement process. They are used to identify improvement opportunities and prioritize them in terms of their expected return for the organization. Data are also used to clarify expected results of performance improvement efforts and to specify outcomes that should be reached. Qualitative data are often used to determine specific performance improvement team membership, and return-on-investment data are used to determine the appropriate application of resources for the team. Finally, monitoring data are used to provide leadership with oversight of the team, to ensure that improvements are implemented appropriately, and to see that gains become permanent and a stable part of organization performance.

Genuine performance improvement relies on a systematic approach to the use of data in all phases of the process. Effective, accurate use of data forms the foundation for sustained, substantial improvement in organizational performance.

## References

1. Cupello JM: A new paradigm for measuring TQM progress. *Quality Progress* 27(5):79–84, 1994.

2. Isgar T, Ranney J, Grinnell S: Team leaders: The key to quality. *Training and Development* 48:45–47, 1994.

3. Stepnick L: *In the Line of Fire: The Coming Public Scrutiny of Hospital and Health System Quality.* Washington, DC: The Healthcare Advisory Board, Advisory Board Company, 1994.

4. Cound DM: *A Leader's Journey to Quality*. Milwaukee: ASQC Quality Press, 1992.

5. Gaucher EJ, Coffey RJ: *Total Quality in Health Care: From Theory to Practice*. San Francisco: Jossey-Bass Publishers, 1993.

6. Luebbe RL, Snavely BK: Making effective team decisions with consensus building tools. *Industrial Management* 9:1–7, 1997.

7. Wright DW, Brauchle PE: Teaming up for quality. *Training and Development* 48:67–73, 1994.

8. Katz JM, Green E: *Managing Quality: A Guide to System-Wide Performance Management in Health Care*, 2nd ed. St Louis: Mosby, 1997.

9. Cordero R: Technical professionals on cross functional teams. *The Journal of Product Innovation* 11:22–29, 1998.

10. Cupello JM: The gentle art of chartering a team. *Quality Progress* 28(9):83–87, 1995.

11. Miles GH: Guidelines for organizing employee TQM teams. *IE Solutions* 28:36–39, 1996.

12. Beck JD, Yeager NM: How to prevent teams from failing. *Quality Progress* 29(3):27–31, 1996.

13. Manz AB, Cheney HP, Sims CC: Teams and TQM. *Business Horizons* 37:16–25, 1994.

14. Henry JE, Hartzler M: Virtual teams: Today's reality, today's challenge. *Quality Progress* 30(5):108–110, 1997.

15. McLaughlin CP, Kaluzny AD: *Continuous Quality Improvement in Health Care*. Gaithersburg, MD: Aspen Publications, 1994.

16. Hitchcock DE, Willard M: Measuring team progress. *Journal for Quality and Participation* 9:12–18, 1992.

# CHAPTER 3:

# Data Collection

Christine McGreevey, RN, MS
Associate Project Director
Division of Research
Joint Commission on Accreditation of Healthcare
Organizations
Oakbrook Terrace, Illinois

Kwan Y. Lee, PhD, SM
Project Director
Division of Research
Joint Commission on Accreditation of Healthcare
Organizations
Oakbrook Terrace, Illinois

The DRIP (data-rich, information-poor) syndrome paralyzes the performance improvement efforts of many health care organizations.[1] The old quality assurance (QA) model in health care was based on the use of many performance measures that were often department specific. The newer performance improvement (PI) model is based on the theory of continuous quality improvement (CQI) and the use of performance measures that are more patient focused and cross-divisional, involving the work of physicians, nurses, social workers, psychologists, technicians, and others on the health care team. However, many organizations have had difficulty migrating from the QA model to the PI model, and consequently they are doing a little of both. This can equate to a data collection burden and a waste of precious health care resources.

This chapter examines important steps in establishing an organizationwide data collection process that works within the PI model. It also includes information on various data sources and how to evaluate the quality of data, as well as tools to be used in documenting the overall process.

## Documenting the Data Collection Plan

Parsimonious data collection will help health care organizations decrease their data collection burden and save resources. The "law of parsimony" comes from Ockham's razor, a fourteenth-century dictum by English philosopher William of Ockham that entities should not be multiplied needlessly. This rule has been interpreted to mean that the simplest of two or more competing theories is preferable, and that explanations for unknown phenomena should first be attempted in terms of what is already known. This concept is germane to a health care organization's data collection practices, which underlie or support leaders' expectations, plans, and process management to systematically measure, assess, and improve the quality of the organization's governance, management, clinical, and support activities. This includes helping staff to stop collecting data that are no longer useful, but are still collected because "we've always done it," and to prevent or decrease duplicative data collection.

One way to ensure that data collection activities are as effective and efficient as possible is to document all such activities within an organization so they can be evaluated. This documentation will include a data inventory, a data dictionary, and a matrix of data element sources for new performance measures.

### Data Inventory

A first step to data parsimony is to develop a data inventory of all data currently being collected for performance improvement purposes (discussed in Chapter 1, page 3). This task may be assigned to someone functioning in the quality management role or to someone from administration or information services. This person may distribute a data inventory questionnaire to all department managers, asking them to list all data contained in logbooks, records, files, and databases maintained in their departments. Included in the inventory would be the definition for each type of data and the reason(s) for collecting it. Figure 3–1 (page 41) provides a sample tool that can be used to create a data inventory.

### Organizationwide Data Dictionary

Once all the sources of data are known from the data inventory process, it is necessary to go back and ask questions about the data being collected. By cataloging the data in a standardized, coordinated, and readily available format, a data dictionary can be developed. This dictionary is a listing of all the data elements collected, with information regarding each element's definition and other important factors, such as storage, ownership, who is responsible for obtaining the data, users, and so on. The dictionary becomes a directory of the organization's data

| Name of Database, Logbook, Records, or Files | Data Structure | Format for Data Entry | Patient Population(s) | Retention Policy |
|---|---|---|---|---|
| *CCU Logbook* | ☑ Manual<br>☐ Electronic | ☑ Coded<br>☐ Descriptive text | ☑ Inpatient<br>☐ Outpatient<br>☐ Emergency<br>☐ Other | ☐ Retain<br>☑ Modify<br>☐ Discontinue<br>Notes: *Convert to electronic database* |
| *Incident Reports* | ☑ Manual<br>☐ Electronic | ☐ Coded<br>☑ Descriptive text | ☑ Inpatient<br>☑ Outpatient<br>☑ Emergency<br>☑ Other | ☐ Retain<br>☑ Modify<br>☐ Discontinue<br>Notes: *Attempt to codify some data* |
|  | ☐ Manual<br>☐ Electronic | ☐ Coded<br>☐ Descriptive text | ☐ Inpatient<br>☐ Outpatient<br>☐ Emergency<br>☐ Other | ☐ Retain<br>☐ Modify<br>☐ Discontinue<br>Notes: _____ |

**Figure 3–1. Sample Data Inventory Questionnaire**

This form can be distributed to department managers to determine what data are already being collected within a health care organization and whether those data are useful to performance improvement activities.

resources. More importantly, it can be used to identify data redundancies, data definition inconsistencies across the organization, and data that are no longer useful. Figure 3–2 (page 42) is an example of a tool that can be used to compile an organizationwide data dictionary.

Both a data inventory and a data dictionary can increase efficiency and bring cost savings to the data collection process. When a need arises for a new data element(s), the person in charge of the data dictionary should work with those involved to determine the most cost-effective and reliable method to obtain the data, making sure that the data are not already being collected elsewhere.

## Matrix of Data Element Sources

When a new performance measure is identified for an organization, an evaluation of the required data elements for the measure needs to take place to determine what is currently collected, what adaptations may need to be made to currently collected data, and whether new data elements need to be added to the organizationwide data dictionary. Creating a matrix, such as the one in Figure 3–3 (page 43), is a good first step for evaluating each of the data elements required for the new measure. Figure 3–4 (page 44) shows a flowchart of the evaluation process.

| Data Element | Definition | Data Sources | Ownership | Use | Security or Privacy Limits | Retention Policy |
|---|---|---|---|---|---|---|
| Bedside procedure | Includes invasive procedures performed at bedside by physician, such as<br>• central line<br>• arterial line<br>• Swan Ganz catheter<br>• temporary pacemaker<br>• endotracheal intubation<br>• tracheostomy<br>• bronchoscopy | • Column in the CCU logbook<br>• Patient medical records<br>• Central supply charges (billing data) | CCU staff | • Assess acuity levels<br>• Audit charges | • Confidential, for internal staff use only<br>• Billing purposes | ❑ Retain<br>☑ Modify<br>❑ Discontinue<br><br>Notes: CCU logbook will be converted to electronic database for data sharing with infection control and central supply department |
| Patient fall | Patient drops from a higher to a lower level or position with or without resulting injury | • Incident reports<br>• Patient medical records | • All staff<br>• Risk manager | • Quality care measure<br>• Prevention | • Confidential, for internal staff use only<br>• ORYX measure for Joint Commission | ❑ Retain<br>☑ Modify<br>❑ Discontinue<br><br>Notes: Parts of the incident report will be converted to an electronic database |
| Physical restraint episode | Any type of physical or mechanical device used to limit movement, physical activity, or normal access in order to protect the patient (client) from self or others | • Restraint reports<br>• Patient medical records | • All staff<br>• Risk manager | • Quality care measure<br>• Prevention | Confidential, for internal staff use only | ☑ Retain<br>❑ Modify<br>❑ Discontinue |

**Figure 3–2. Sample Data Dictionary Questionnaire**

This form can be used to compile the necessary information about all data being collected within an organization. Some of the information will already be available from the data inventory process.

| Data Element | Potential Data Sources | Actual Data Sources | Responsibility for Collection | Collection Method | Storage/ Retention System(s) | Most Efficient Collection Method |
|---|---|---|---|---|---|---|
| Medical record number | Patient medical record; admitting | Hospital Information System (HIS) | Data entry by Dept of Admissions | Electronic | SMS (HIS) | Download from HIS |
| Admission date | Face sheet of medical record; billing data; UB-92 | HIS | Data entry by Dept of Admissions | Electronic | SMS (HIS) | Download from HIS |
| ASA-PS score | Operating room record; surgical software scheduling system | Anesthesia Record Sheet | OR staff | Manual | Column added to OR's scheduling logbook to capture | OR staff to copy logbook pages each month; send to QI staff |
| Birthweight (of infant born during this admission) | Patient medical record; electronic birth certificate; newborn nursery logbook | | | | | |

**Figure 3–3. Data Element Source and Collection Matrix**

A matrix such as this can be used as part of the process shown in Figure 3–4 to identify an organization's data sources and collection methods.

# Data Sources

Conducting organizationwide data inventories and creating data dictionaries are not simple tasks and often require significant resources (such as staff time) to complete. However, they will eventually lead to the efficient use of resources associated with data collection and performance improvement. Data can be collected from electronic sources (such as computerized administrative data), manual data abstraction of clinical records, and administration of survey tools.

## Electronic Data Collection

Many health care organizations already have access to electronic data that come from the admission and/or billing process. The utility of billing data as a data source for performance improvement activities has been debated among health services researchers for many years, but it is certainly a useful data source for its ease of access. Some facilities use a combination of billing data and data abstracted from clinical records or other electronic sources within the organization. Some other potential electronic sources include "homegrown" databases or spreadsheets, medication administration record software packages, and laboratory software packages. The computerized patient record has been proposed as a data source for years, but it is not widely used at this time.

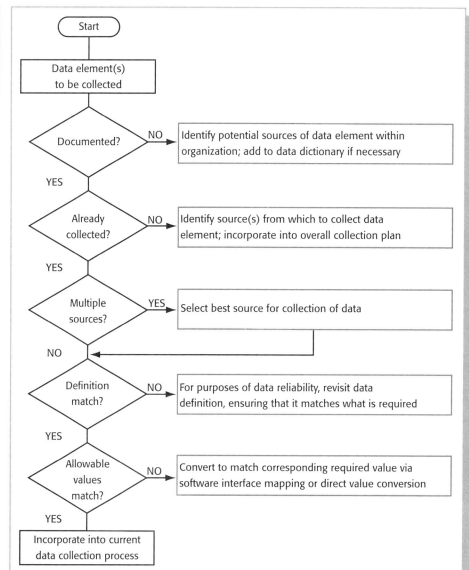

**Figure 3–4. Process for Identifying Data Element Sources**
This flowchart illustrates the process for identifying sources and collection methods of data elements for new performance measures. For example, a performance measurement system's data element "Expected Source of Payment" had allowable values of (1) PPO; (2) HMO; (3) Commercial; (4) Medicare; (5) Medicaid; (6) Self; and (7) Other. The hospital captured this information in its UB–92 claim values. It mapped those values to the measurement system's values. For example, the value "12" was PPO on the UB–92 claim form and it became "1" for the measurement systems allowable value equal to PPO for their database. This movement of data and required edit/change were performed electronically prior to data submission to the measurement system.

Even if an organization has access to many electronic data sources, data are often incompatible, and combining or transferring data to where they are needed becomes next to impossible. The cost involved in customizing software programs to automatically transfer data from one source to another (software interface programs) can run into thousands of dollars or more. Many health care organizations have purchased or created software packages that do not "talk to one another," so data sharing is impeded. Organizations need to investigate internal data compatibility or transportability before purchasing or creating new software packages. To ensure data quality, data collection software is often developed with protocols in place or data entry edits to prevent entry errors. However, data electronically transferred bypass the data entry edits. Testing is required to ensure that data are transferred correctly when software interface programs are used.

### Manual Data Collection

Data are often collected manually by abstracting data from medical records and other paper forms used by the organization. Automating these paper data sources can be done using direct data entry at the point of service or by retrospective data entry from the paper form (hard copy). Electronic data can be shared more expeditiously than manual data and are easier to manipulate for data analysis, if needed. The following are typical hard copy data sources that may be useful for PI activities.

*Patient Medical Record.* For every patient treated, hospitals, long term care facilities, ambulatory care centers, physicians' offices, behavioral health centers, and home care organizations all keep a handwritten record of events, referred to in this book as the *patient medical record*. It is compiled by physicians and other health care professionals of a variety of patient health information, such as assessment findings, treatment details, and progress notes.

Health informatics is a career field centered around patient health information. A registered health information technician (RHIT) has a two-year degree, and a registered health information administrator (RHIA) has a four-year degree in health information management (HIM). In hospital and ambulatory treatment centers, HIM professionals (coders) read through a patient's clinical record, abstract data, and translate those data into *International Classification of Diseases, Ninth Edition, Clinical Modification* (ICD-9-CM) diagnosis and procedure codes for hospitals or current procedural terminology (CPT) codes for ambulatory surgical procedures and treatments. Medicare and other insurance companies reimburse for health care services using these codes, which were primarily designed as standardized classification systems. Medicare pays hospitals by diagnosis-related groups (DRGs) from a software program called a "grouper" that considers the patient's primary diagnosis (what brought the patient to the hospital for treatment), comorbidities, and treatment received during hospitalization, and then pays a flat fee per the assigned DRG group (such as DRG 129 for heart failure without procedures). Clinical record data are costly to abstract; the use of computerized patient records may counteract this labor-intensive process in the future.

*Logbooks.* Many departments or units keep paper logbooks to record such things as patient admissions or visits, including the date and time of arrival, the reason for the admission or visit, the patient's room number(s), what procedures were performed, discharge date and time, and so on. A nursing home may keep a logbook of residents' weekly weights or the activities residents have participated in, with additional notations that are pertinent to each. If additional data are required for a PI project, a column(s) may be added to these logbooks to facilitate ease of data collection.

Logbooks can be efficiently transformed into electronic files by using spreadsheet or database software packages that are readily available and easily customized to an organization's special needs. Once the hard copy data are computerized, sharing data with appropriate health care team members is easily facilitated (as long as the same software for data collection is available to all those needing the information), especially through network servers or floppy disks. Staff members should be aware of the need for appropriate backup files and frequent data saving.

*Specially Designed Data Collection Tools.* At times, manual data collection may be facilitated by using a specially created tool containing closed-ended questions and a predefined choice of responses (such as asking a patient to rate his or her level of pain on a scale of 0 to 10, with 0 equal to no pain and 10 equal to excruciating pain, or asking for the best answer from four choices). Then, data can be entered into an electronic file (spreadsheet or database) or other information system for efficient and effective data analysis and information sharing. The Health Care Financing Administration's (HCFA's) Minimum Data Set (MDS) for long term care residents and OASIS database for home health patients are examples of specially designed data collection tools for periodic patient assessments.

Figure 3–5 (page 47) shows an example of a tool designed for collecting data for a measure regarding primary bloodstream infections (PBIs) related to central lines (an infection rate measure). Data collection for this measure is a little complicated, partly due to the varying definitions of a PBI and partly because the patient may transfer from unit to unit during the admission period and needs to be tracked. The tool in Figure 3–5 can be used to gather all the data needed in one place for later data entry. Note that data must be collected not only on those patients having a PBI due to a central line (the measure's numerator or event of interest), but also on patients having a central line who do not have a PBI (the measure's denominator or population includes all patients having a central line). The number of days patients had central lines in place is required, so beginning and ending dates are included on the data collection form.

*Checklists.* A checklist is another form for gathering data. An example of a checklist might be a discharge summary sheet of instructions to be given to a patient upon discharge from the emergency department. Sometimes a checklist will have blank lines for physicians or nurses to write specific instructions given to a particular patient and then checked off when the instructions have been delivered. For example, in long term care, a checklist is often used to record a resident's skin integrity on a weekly basis.

*Records of Events.* Often paper forms are used to gather information and can be modified to collect needed data in a routine and reliable way. For example, patient assessment forms can be used to calculate composite scores or values for the overall health status of patients. Some performance measures can be derived based on

Patient ID #_____  Patient Name:_____

Admission Date:_____  Time:_____am pm          Age:_____

Discharge Date:_____  Time:_____am pm

**Infection Control Indicator #33:** Central or umbilical line and primary bloodstream infection

Population:     All inpatients with a central or umbilical line in place.

Exclusions:     1) Patients with line inserted only in the OR/PARR time frame.

                     2) Patients with LOS < 48 hours.

**ICU TYPE:**

[BURN] [CVCU] [CCU] [MICU] [MedSurg] [Neonatal] [Neuro] [Ped] [Resp] [Surg] [Trauma] [Non-ICU Nursing Unit]

Line Insertion Date:_____  **OR**          Line Present on Admission?          ❏ Yes          ❏ No

Line Removal **OR** Patient Transfer Date:_____

**ICU TYPE:**

[BURN] [CVCU] [CCU] [MICU] [MedSurg] [Neonatal] [Neuro] [Ped] [Resp] [Surg] [Trauma] [Non-ICU Nursing Unit]

Line Insertion Date:_____  **OR**          Line Present on Admission?          ❏ Yes          ❏ No

Line Removal **OR** Patient Transfer Date:_____

**ICU TYPE:**

[BURN] [CVCU] [CCU] [MICU] [MedSurg] [Neonatal] [Neuro] [Ped] [Resp] [Surg] [Trauma] [Non-ICU Nursing Unit]

Line Insertion Date:_____  **OR**          Line Present on Admission?          ❏ Yes          ❏ No

Line Removal **OR** Patient Transfer Date:_____

***ICU Where Primary Bloodstream Infection Originated***

| **Infection** | **Primary Bloodstream** |
|---|---|
| **Originated** | **Infection Identified** |
| 0\|_____ | \|48 hours |
| *(Line in place)* | *(Line may or may not be in place)* |

**PRIMARY BLOODSTREAM INFECTION?**          ❏ Yes          ❏ No

*If yes, then check the following if patient had:*

LABORATORY SEPSIS:

❏ recognized pathogen cultured (blood) not related to infection at another site

❏ hypotension

❏ fever (>38°C)

❏ chills

CLINICAL SEPSIS:

Patient has at least one of the following with no other recognized cause:

❏ fever (>38°C)

❏ hypotension (< 90 systolic)

❏ oliguria (< 20 cc/hr)

Common skin contaminant (e.g., diptheroids, *Bacillus* sp.,

*Propionibacterium* sp., coagulase-neg. Staph., or micrococci)

❏ cultured from 2+ blood cultures drawn on separate occasions

❏ cultured from at least 1 blood culture & MD institutes antimicrobial therapy

❏ Blood culture not done

❏ No apparent infection at another site

❏ MD institutes treatment for sepsis

❏ Positive antigen test on blood (e.g., *H. Influenzae, S. Pneumoniae, N. Meningitis*, or Group B streptococcus) AND  signs & symptoms and positive lab results are *not* related to infection at another site

Plus, if patient is less than one year old:

❏ fever (>38°C)          ❏ hypothermia (<37°C)          ❏ apnea          ❏ bradycardia

**Figure 3–5. Sample Data Collection Form for a Primary Bloodstream Infection Measure**

This form was specifically designed to collect data pertaining to a high-risk, high-volume, problem-prone population. The form includes information for both the numerator (patients with a PBI caused by a central line) and the denominator (total number of patients with central lines) for the measure.

a patient's assessment score change from admission to discharge. Forms such as operating room records and birth records also fall into this category.

Forms must be made useful to the organization's specific services and popula-tions. For example, one hospital had trouble collecting the ASA-PS (American Society of Anesthesiologists—Physical Status) classification score for patients undergoing invasive gastrointestinal procedures under anesthesia outside the tra-ditional operating room setting. The ASA-PS score is often used as an important risk-adjustment factor. The hospital redesigned its special procedures record form to capture this data element and to record the patient's vital signs during the pro-cedures. Anesthesiologists trained physicians performing these procedures to determine patients' appropriate ASA-PS classifications preoperatively.

A psychiatric hospital used an admission behavior assessment form to begin capturing needed clinical information that it had difficulty collecting on a routine basis as part of the clinical record. This increased the consistency and quality of data needed for performance monitoring and improving processes. Plus, it allowed the hospital to repeat the assessment at various intervals during the treat-ment period to assess the success of the treatment plan.

## Survey Data Collection

Another source for performance measurement data comes from survey tools, which can be used to capture patient satisfaction or patient perception of care data after health care services have been rendered. Survey data can be obtained through personal interviews, via telephone conversations, or by mailing a survey instrument to the patient's home. Mailing surveys is the most common approach. Health care organizations may do the mailings themselves, or they may give a list of patients to a third party that specializes in these types of surveys. Similarly, organizations may receive the survey responses directly from patients, or the responses may be mailed to a third party who will perform the data entry and analysis. Generally, the survey tool should be sent soon after the discharge or serv-ice date.

Many experts propose that a response rate of 50% to 70% is needed to ensure that the results can be interpreted meaningfully.[2,3] Often, mailed survey data are sent to a sample of the population of interest to save costs (sampling is discussed later in this chapter, pages 50–52). For example, information taken from sampled survey data having less than a 20% response rate will likely lack any credible statistics of the population as a whole.[3] Therefore, an organization may need to brainstorm ways to increase response rates. This may mean shortening the survey tool so it can be filled out more quickly and easily or offering some incentive to those who respond. In addition, those who do not respond need to be examined to study ran-domness of nonresponses. Sometimes the sample size can be adjusted to devote additional resources to developing a better-designed survey tool and increasing the response rate.

# Factors Affecting Implementation of Data Collection

Although the actual plan for data collection is important, several additional factors can influence the success of implementation. These include the organizationwide approach (which may include barriers) to sharing data, data security, who collects the data, and the need for pilot testing.

## Common Barriers to Data Sharing

Data should be shared throughout the organization, as appropriate. Resistance to data sharing can create "data dynasties" and may stem from a perceived power base, attempts to conceal poor performance, or tight departmental budgets. Leaders should encourage data sharing by showing support of and commitment to efficient collection and use of data. One way to do this is to position in an upper level of management a data administrator who reports directly to senior management.

## Data Security

Data should be readily available, yet protected from unauthorized disclosure or misuse. Security policies and procedures should address every point at which data can be accessed. User responsibilities include password protection, physical security of computers, and protection of hard copy reports containing sensitive information.

Staff responsible for information systems need to protect access to computer files and database management systems, and to determine whether each user has access to modify or only view data. In the past, data have been kept so secure that they were not available to appropriate staff members. A balance between security and utility must be weighed by an organization's leaders. Often, the staff working with patients are the ones with the key information to improve processes. However, without information they often are unaware of any problems.

## Responsibility for Data Collection

Data should be collected by whoever has the easiest and most reliable access to them within the organization. Training data collectors is a critical step to gathering complete and accurate data while minimizing abstractor-to-abstractor variation. Staff need to clearly understand the required data elements and their definitions in order to collect accurate data. Additionally, they need to know when to collect the data (such as concurrently at admission, prior to a procedure, after a procedure, or retrospectively after the patient is discharged) and how frequently (daily, weekly, monthly, quarterly, and so forth). If an organization has contracted with a software vendor or performance measurement system, training seminars or self-instruction books may be offered to help data collectors better understand the specified performance measures and the need for complete and accurate data collection to obtain valid and reliable information.

---

**ORYX Tip: A Sampling Strategy Technique**

For the ORYX Core Measure Pilot Study, sampling is *not recommended* when the measure's population for a particular health care organization is less than 50 cases per month. (Here, monthly data are assessed because that is the basic unit of analysis for ORYX data.) If a health care organization does average more than 50 cases per month, then sampling is an option for that measure. The Joint Commission recommends that the number of cases in the sample generally represents at least 20% of the organization's measure population, with a *minimum* sample requirement of 50 cases and a *maximum* sample of 200 cases being required.

---

*(continued on page 51)*

*Pilot Testing*

When a new data collection form is introduced or new data elements are to be collected, it may be beneficial to pilot test the process. The new approach can be introduced to a limited area of the organization, such as a single department or unit. Any problem areas can be identified during the pilot test, and the form or method of data collection can be enhanced prior to organizationwide implementation. When the pilot version is complete and working smoothly, it can be expanded to the rest of the organization.[4]

## Appropriate Sampling Techniques

One way to reduce the data collection effort behind performance measures is to use a sampling technique. Sampling is a basic statistical tool that draws a limited number of measurements from a larger source (population), and then analyzes those measurements to estimate characteristics of that population. However, statistically valid sampling methodology is required to obtain valid and reliable measurement data and to ensure the credibility of the information gleaned from that data. Sampling error is the unavoidable potential for error whenever a random sample rather than a whole population is used, due to the smaller size of the sample. The key, then, is to reduce the amount of sampling error as much as possible. Limiting sampling error is linked to selecting the correct sample size for a population and using random sampling to determine the sample group.

*When Is Sampling a Viable Option?*

Each performance measure needs to be examined separately to determine whether it is a candidate for sampling. A statistician can help an organization decide whether sampling is a feasible option on a measure-by-measure basis, because some performance measures tend to have large populations (such as the number of residents and the rate of falls) and others have very small populations (such as the number of falls and the injury rate from falls). An organization may be able to partially sample some measures, yet it may need to include all eligible data (100% sample) for other measures.

*How Are Sample Sizes Determined?*

To correctly infer the characteristics of a population from a sample, an appropriate sample size should be achieved. To determine sample size, several factors should be considered, including the population size, the anticipated rate for the population, and the probability of making an incorrect decision about the population. In general, the more variation that exists within the population, the larger the sample size needed to make correct inference about the population. Most introductory statistics books provide discussion about sample size determination.

## How Should Representative Samples Be Selected?

To ensure that the sampled data represent the organization's measure population, sample cases should be identified using acceptable techniques such as the following:

- *Simple random sampling* is a process in which a predetermined number of cases from a population as a whole is selected for review. It is predicated on the idea that each case in the population has an equal probability of being included in the sample.

- *Systematic random sampling* is a process in which one case is selected randomly, and the next cases are selected according to a fixed interval; (for example, every fifth patient who undergoes a surgical procedure).

Other sampling techniques, including those listed here, also may be used, but they can increase the possibility of sampling errors:

- *Stratified sampling* is a two-step process. First, the population is stratified into groups, and then a simple random sample is taken from each group.

- *Cluster sampling* is a process in which the population is divided into groups, and then some of the groups are selected to be sampled. For example, to save costs in direct patient interviews held in patient households, the Minnesota Heart Study divided the state of Minnesota into geographically compact regions or clusters. It then selected a random sample of clusters for the study, and several interviewers were sent to each cluster selected.[5]

- *Judgment sampling* is a process in which experts in the subject matter select certain cases to be sampled. Unlike the previously mentioned "probability" sampling techniques, this form of sampling is considered a "nonprobability sample." It is likely that the sample group will not represent the population's characteristics; however, the experts selecting the cases may be trying to change a particular process. For example, a study may attempt to determine the reasons women having acute myocardial infarction are less likely to receive thrombolysis than men of the same age.

## How Should Sampling Processes Be Implemented?

A simple method for selecting a systematic random sample would be to obtain a list of patients in the order in which they were discharged or treated, count the number of patients on the list, and divide by the number needed for the sample size. The resulting number will be the interval between one patient on the list and the next patient on the list who is to be selected for sampling. For example, if the list has 300 patients and the required sample size for the measure is 50 cases, every sixth (300/50 = 6) patient record would be selected for data collection. To make sure each patient has an equal chance (randomness) of being selected, those performing the selection may roll a die. For example, if the die comes up six, starting at the sixth patient record, every fourth patient record is selected for data collection, until 50 cases have been chosen. If necessary, one can rotate up to the top of

(continued from page 50)

Commission by the transmission deadline (four months after the end of each quarter).

An organization should look closely at its missing data problems, including how many cases should be collected each month and sent to its measurement system. The organization should compare its numbers with those its measurement system reports in its comparative feedback reports.

For example, an organization might compare its own internal data with the data on the Joint Commission's ORYX Pre-Survey Report™ (distributed only to those organizations undergoing a survey). This process is similar to balancing a checkbook—personal records are checked against the bank's statement so any inconsistencies can be rectified. If a checkbook is not balanced regularly, problems can occur. The same is true for any organization sending data to a third party; it needs to verify the accuracy and completeness of the data transactions (counts of what was sent versus what was received and reported).

the list to get the required number of cases. A simple random sample is best obtained using one of the many available computer programs (often statistical software or database software) that offer "random number generators."

## What Types of Survey Error Can Occur?

Four potential survey errors can occur[6]:

- *Selection bias* results from the exclusion of certain groups of subjects so they have no chance of being selected for the sample;

- *Nonresponse bias* results when a large percentage of subjects are unwilling to respond to a survey;

- *Sampling error* refers to the chance differences from one sample to another, although both should be equally representative of the population; and

- *Measurement error* refers to inaccuracies in the recorded response that occur because of a weakness in question wording, the "halo effect" in a personal interview where the respondent feels compelled to please the interviewer, or a lack of effort made by the respondent.

Survey data that lack credibility and objectivity may very well be useless information. If decisions are being made based on survey data, a basic understanding of sampling methodologies, response rates, and survey errors is necessary to make the correct decisions.

## Data Quality

A key question for health care organizations should be, "How do you know your data are valid?" The accuracy and completeness of the data collected have a direct relationship to the validity and reliability of the data analysis findings. Although this is addressed earlier in the chapter, it is worth repeating. If all data are not present, or if data are collected one way by one person and another way by another person, the conclusions based on those data will be erroneous. First, education and training must be given to those who are responsible for collecting the data. Many workers will perform better if they understand the hows and whys of what they are doing and the importance of their work to those using the data.

Second, periodic validation of data quality should occur to ensure that the collected data are accurate and complete. Any inconsistencies should be identified and removed. A common knee-jerk reaction is to "blame the worker," when what is needed for improvement are management processes for retraining or educating the workers involved, allowing more time for data collection, redesigning data collection tools, and so on.

### Validating Data Quality

There are many ways to evaluate data quality. Some measures require special validation techniques, depending on their unique characteristics. How an

*(continued on page 53)*

organization decides to validate its data is distinctive to its operation and needs. The following are some suggestions of commonly used techniques:

- *Cross-reference checking of results between similar or complementary measures.* One hospital participated in HCFA's[1] acute myocardial infarction project and also the National Registry of Myocardial Infarction study. The hospital validated its data by comparing similar measures from each study to determine whether the number of cases and the measure rates were the same. When they were not, they were investigated to uncover the causes of the discrepancies, which were often slightly different data definitions or measure exclusion requirements between the two entities.

- *Periodic reabstraction by a different person than the usual data collector for a sample group of patient records.* This approach is commonly used for manually abstracted data on a monthly or quarterly basis. A certain number or percentage of patient records are pulled at random, and someone reabstracts the data using the same data collection tool used by the usual data collector to determine an error rate. This method is referred to as "interrator or inter-observer reliability." Frequently occurring errors are investigated to determine possible causes, and actions are taken to prevent the error from recurring. Some organizations select a statistically valid sample size to reabstract; others simply select a small, manageable number of records. The theory in the latter case is that even evaluating only 10 to 15 records a quarter is better than nothing.

- *Data collection software.* The use of data collection software allows for built-in edits to promote data integrity. This is a benefit of using an automated approach to collect data because some errors can be found and corrected at the point of data entry. Also, missing data can be prevented by software prompts to the user for needed data.

- *Review of vendor reports.* If a health care organization electronically transmits its data to a third-party vendor or performance measurement system, it is likely to receive some type of transmission report detailing the number of records received and any potential errors that may need to be corrected. Reviewing these reports and making timely corrections when needed will help improve data quality.

- *Continuous tracking.* It is a good idea to track data quality findings on an ongoing basis, along with any improvements used to refine the data collection process. This helpful information can be used by future workers and managers who may be new to the process. Also, it can give credence to the quality of the data when someone (such as managers, leaders, the board of directors, or surveyors) asks, "How do you know that this report is accurate and that the data are valid?"

- *Networking with other health care organizations that use the same or similar performance measures.* It is a good idea to ask other organizations how they validate their data, and to share lessons learned. Also, measurement systems do

*(continued from page 52)*

mit the data in a special electronic data interchange (EDI) file to the Joint Commission by the deadline.

Many measurement systems send data to the Joint Commission earlier than the deadline date to correct any errors or rejected data noted on the Joint Commission's Transmission Reports, which are produced after each data transmission. Accepting a health care organization's data late in this process is virtually impossible for most measurement systems because they would have to redo their comparison analyses.

On the other hand, some measurement systems are able to incorporate a health care organization's late data submissions, including submissions for correcting data previously sent in error. For ORYX purposes, the system may not be able to transmit these new data to the Joint Commission (if the deadline has passed), but it may be able to correct its own data and provide the organization with more correct information in its comparative feedback reports. In this case, the health care organization can show the more updated comparative feedback reports to a surveyor and explain that the information is more correct than what is in the ORYX Pre-Survey Report™.

their own data quality checks and audits of organization data. They are most likely the best source of information for checking the validity of data used in measures.

### Data Submissions to a Measurement System

An important factor of data quality that directly affects the resulting usefulness of the reports derived from third-party vendors or performance measurement systems is the timely transmission of data to those performing data analysis and creating the feedback information.

Health care organizations are likely to submit data (billing, financial, and so forth) in various formats to various entities at certain intervals. Data should be exact and accurate depictions of patient care, reflecting the following elements:

- Correct patient demographic information;
- Correct time period of the services provided;
- Correct list of services/products provided to the patient; and
- Transmission to the correct vendor.

## Summary

Data used to make informed decisions about the delivery of health care should be of the highest quality possible so that the right decisions can be made. Maintaining data integrity requires involvement of the staff participating in the data collection process, the data vendors or measurement systems, and the staff who use the data. Organization leaders need to ensure that their decisions are based on valid and reliable information.

## References

1. Goodwin S: Data rich, information poor (DRIP) syndrome: Is there a treatment? *QRC Advisor* 12(2):1–5, 1995.

2. Carey R: How to choose a patient survey system. *Journal on Quality Improvement* 25(1):20–25, 1995.

3. Fowler F: *Survey Research Methods*, 2nd ed. Newbury Park, CA: Sage Publications, 1993.

4. Laudon K, Laudon JP: *Management Information Systems*. New York: Macmillan, 1991.

5. Rosner B: *Fundamentals of Biostatistics*. New York: Duxbury Press, 1995.

6. Berenson M, Levine D: *Basic Business Statistics: Concepts and Applications*, 7th ed. Upper Saddle River, NJ: Prentice Hall, 1999.

# CHAPTER 4:

# Tools for Data Analysis

Christine McGreevey, RN, MS
Associate Project Director
Division of Research
Joint Commission on Accreditation of Healthcare
Organizations
Oakbrook Terrace, Illinois

Kwan Y. Lee, PhD, SM
Project Director
Division of Research
Joint Commission on Accreditation of Healthcare
Organizations
Oakbrook Terrace, Illinois

The U.S. Congress established the Malcolm Baldrige National Quality Award program in 1987 to recognize U.S. organizations for their achievements in quality and business performance and to raise awareness about the importance of quality and performance excellence as a competitive edge. Health care quality is difficult to measure without attempting to quantify it. Indicators (performance measures) of quality need to be in place and are thought to be necessary if an organization is to deliver high-quality care.

## Developing Indicators

Some organizations have trouble determining what indicators to use. The financial manager of a hospice organization was once heard to ask, "What quality measures can we possibly measure? All our patients die—our

mortality rates would be 100%!" Health care executives and managers are used to financial measures—accounts payable, accounts receivable, income, expenses, return on investment, and so forth. But as the business world has realized, financial measures do not tell the whole story about an organization. Many organizations use a "balanced scorecard" approach to measurement, using a few strategic measures in four domains[1]:

- Key internal process measures;

- Key financial measures;

- Innovation and improvement measures; and

- Customer satisfaction on operational measures.

The hospice financial manager only focused on one aspect of the organization's services and may not have understood the operational challenges that exist. Of course, mortality rates would not be a measure of quality for hospice patients; organizations providing such services should focus on measures that are important to their patients' quality of life. These may include process measures regarding patient assessment for safety needs, dietary needs, pain control needs, and appropriate activity levels. One important hospice outcome measure might be whether the patient is able to stay at home with adequate supportive care during the hospice period and avoid hospitalization. Other important measures could include patient/family satisfaction measures regarding the patient's level of pain control, the relief of gastrointestinal symptoms or other physical symptoms that interfere with the patient's comfort, and a perceived level of medical and emotional support.

Quality indicators should be created with an understanding of how data will be analyzed and interpreted, so the information derived from the data can be used to provide better care to patients. And better care can be a competitive edge. Organizations can link quality and cost, meeting the dual goals of delivering high-quality health care in a cost-effective manner.

Performance measures (indicators) in health care can be taken from any point along the patient care time line: at admission or during treatment, after instructions/education (assessment or survey tools), at discharge, or after the patient is billed. Data collection may occur while the patient is receiving treatment or services (concurrent method) or after the patient is discharged (retrospective method).

Each performance measure comprises various inputs to the process, the care process itself, and the outcome(s) of interest (Figure 4–1, page 57). The outcome of interest may reflect process points or steps in the patient's plan of care (for example, Did the patient receive a prophylactic antibiotic preoperatively? How many minutes prior to the surgical incision was it administered?) or a definitive patient outcome (for example, Did the patient develop a surgical site infection?). A *process measure* focuses on one or more steps that lead to a certain outcome, such as whether preventive skin care was given to patients at risk for developing pressure

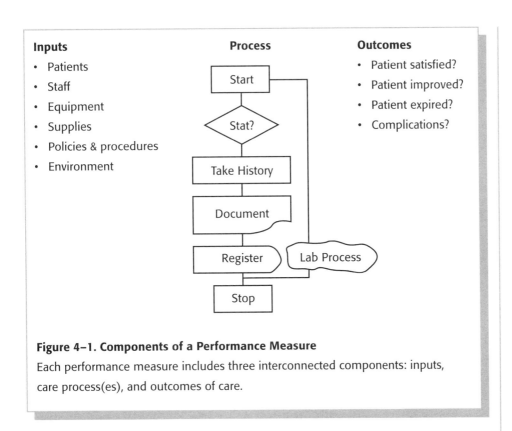

**Inputs**
- Patients
- Staff
- Equipment
- Supplies
- Policies & procedures
- Environment

**Process**

Start

Stat?

Take History

Document

Register

Lab Process

Stop

**Outcomes**
- Patient satisfied?
- Patient improved?
- Patient expired?
- Complications?

**Figure 4–1. Components of a Performance Measure**
Each performance measure includes three interconnected components: inputs, care process(es), and outcomes of care.

ulcers. An *outcome measure* focuses on the result of the performance or nonperformance of the process, such as which patients who did or did not receive care developed pressure ulcers.

By focusing on the process and outcomes of care, measures can direct more attention to the desires of the patient (voice of the customer). This use of performance measurement focuses on "the use of a data-driven scientific approach to change—rather than on a reliance on hunches and tampering"[2] to improve care. Although some people may think that performance measurement focuses on problems (mortality rates, infection rates, patient satisfaction rates, and so forth), others see opportunities to provide better care, make customers more satisfied (or delighted), and gain that competitive edge.

## Turning Data into Information

Once an organization has conceptually quantified high-quality care and collected necessary data, the next step is to analyze the results and take appropriate action as opportunities are identified. Figure 4–2 (page 58) depicts statistical thinking concepts promoted by the American Society of Quality, which states

> Statistical thinking is a philosophy of learning and action based on the following fundamental principles:
>
> • All work occurs in a system of interconnected processes.
>
> • Variation exists in all processes—it is a fact of life.

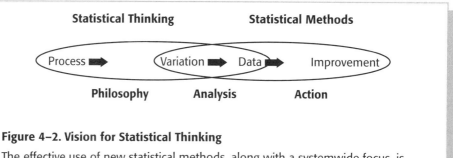

**Figure 4–2. Vision for Statistical Thinking**

The effective use of new statistical methods, along with a systemwide focus, is needed for effecting quality and productivity improvement.

*Source:* Improving Performance Through Statistical Thinking. *Milwaukee, WI: ASQ Quality Press, 1999, p 24. Used with permission.*

- Understanding and reducing variation are keys to success (from Edwards Deming's management philosophy in reducing variation).[3]

Raw data cannot be used to draw conclusions about a process or an outcome. Harvested from medical records, patient survey results, or some other source, raw data need further processing and refinement in order to become useful information to those who manage and deliver patient care. The data must be displayed in formats that are conducive to further analysis to identify opportunities to improve care and to examine the results of improvement efforts.

Sometimes raw data are partially processed and displayed in a tabular format in reports. Although these "table data" may be of some use in understanding an organization's performance, those responsible for using and understanding the reports often take those numbers and display them in graphical charts to make the data more user friendly and easier to interpret. Several approaches may be used to create such graphical charts, including paper and pencil, common spreadsheet packages, and statistical software packages. (See the December 1999 issue of *Quality Digest* for a list of available statistical process control software packages.) Some basic statistical knowledge and even creativity are required for successful analysis, display, and use of performance measurement data for the purposes of understanding, forming conclusions, and/or asking more questions about underlying performance. A desirable skill set in the analysis, investigation, planning, and action phases of performance improvement includes having knowledge/experience in health care as well as in performance improvement and data analysis techniques.

## Systems Thinking

Computer pioneer Jay Forrester, a Massachusetts Institute of Technology researcher, is credited with developing the philosophy of systems dynamics in the 1970s. He felt that many of the world's problems had resulted from or worsened because of the policies designed to solve them. He advocated avoiding the "Band-

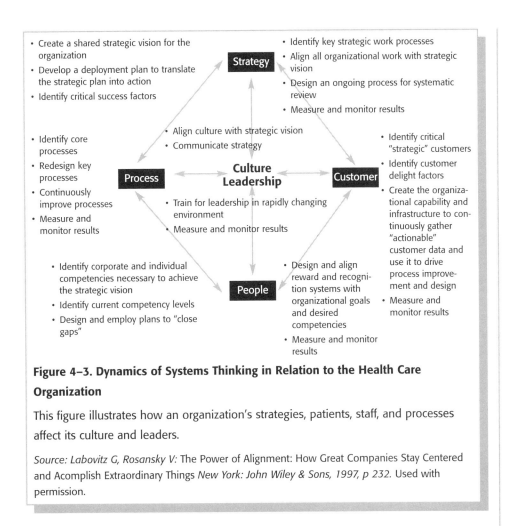

- Create a shared strategic vision for the organization
- Develop a deployment plan to translate the strategic plan into action
- Identify critical success factors

- Identify key strategic work processes
- Align all organizational work with strategic vision
- Design an ongoing process for systematic review
- Measure and monitor results

**Strategy**

- Identify core processes
- Redesign key processes
- Continuously improve processes
- Measure and monitor results

**Process**

- Align culture with strategic vision
- Communicate strategy

**Culture Leadership**

- Train for leadership in rapidly changing environment
- Measure and monitor results

**Customer**

- Identify critical "strategic" customers
- Identify customer delight factors
- Create the organizational capability and infrastructure to continuously gather "actionable" customer data and use it to drive process improvement and design
- Measure and monitor results

- Identify corporate and individual competencies necessary to achieve the strategic vision
- Identify current competency levels
- Design and employ plans to "close gaps"

**People**

- Design and align reward and recognition systems with organizational goals and desired competencies
- Measure and monitor results

**Figure 4–3. Dynamics of Systems Thinking in Relation to the Health Care Organization**

This figure illustrates how an organization's strategies, patients, staff, and processes affect its culture and leaders.

*Source: Labovitz G, Rosansky V: The Power of Alignment: How Great Companies Stay Centered and Acomplish Extraordinary Things New York: John Wiley & Sons, 1997, p 232.* Used with permission.

Aid approach" to solving the symptoms of a problem and instead delving to find the problem's root causes.[4]

An organization's culture and leadership are influenced by its strategies, customers (patients), people (staff), and processes (Figure 4–3, above).[5] Systems thinking involves curiosity (to ask why something is happening), clarity (to determine the cause and effect), compassion (to move from blame to responsibility), choice (to allow for multiple solutions), and courage (to stand in favor of unpopular solutions that work in the long term).[6] Some people may ask, "But isn't health care different, given that patients have different severity levels and extenuating circumstances that make measuring for improvement difficult?" The response is that, although health care is different because patients add to the complexity of performance improvement, too many organizations use that as an excuse not to try to improve.[7]

*Processes Versus Systems*

A *process* may be defined as an interrelated series of activities, actions, events, or steps that transforms inputs into outputs for a particular beneficiary or customer. A *system* is a network of interdependent components that work together to try to accomplish the aim of the system, as in an emergency medical services system.

**Best Use of QI Tools**

Discrete processes (or systems) in which cause-and-effect relationships are observable and occur within a time frame that enables cycling through the Plan-Do-Check-Act wheel.

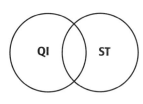

**Best Use of ST Tools**

Dynamic, nonlinear systems (or processes) in which the complexity of interrelated variables and time delays obscure the ability to distinguish root causes and effects

**Figure 4–4. Overlap of Quality Improvement and Systems Thinking Tools**

Although quality improvement (QI) and systems thinking (ST) tools have different purposes, they can complement each other when used in performance improvement efforts.

*Source: Copyright 1993, Bette H. Gardner. Used with permission.*

Peter Senge, a systems thinking expert, has defined a system as a perceived whole whose elements "hang together" because they continually affect each other over time and operate toward a common purpose.[8] In *The Fifth Discipline Fieldbook*, Senge et al explain that there are no right answers for systems problems because the systems' dynamics are an illustration of interdependencies. One must learn to recognize the ramifications and tradeoffs of actions chosen—to begin to explore a systems problem, state the problem, tell the story or stories behind that problem (in a list or graphically), and ask the "five whys" (root cause analysis).[9] For example, complex systems have many interdependent variables, which can be illustrated in a diagram using links and feedback loops. Drawing a picture of the system can help determine whether some of the complexity can be removed without creating havoc elsewhere.

## Tools to Improve Performance and Systems

There is some overlap in performance improvement tools and systems thinking tools (Figure 4–4, above).

### Performance Improvement Tools

Performance improvement tools (also called statistical process control tools) are familiar to most health care organizations and may be nonstatistical or statistical. Nonstatistical tools include brainstorming, multivoting, cause-and-effect diagrams, process flowcharts, algorithms, clinical pathways, and critical pathways. Statistical tools include control charts, histograms, Pareto charts, run charts, and scatter diagrams.

*Brainstorming.* This problem-solving technique uses the collective knowledge of a group whose individual members take turns contributing a large number of ideas without criticism.[10] The following four basic rules govern brainstorming sessions:

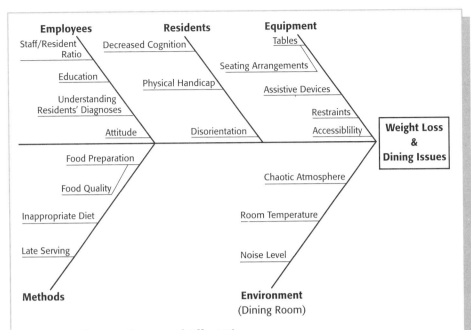

**Figure 4–5. Sample Cause-and-Effect Diagram**

A long term care organization that has a problem with high rates of weight loss among its residents might generate a diagram that looks something like this for the causes found. Each bone in the diagram can contribute to the cause(s) linked to the weight loss problem.

- Consider all ideas. Creative ideas are incomplete in the beginning. The meeting leader/facilitator should allow no criticism of anyone's idea.

- Think of outrageous and off-the-wall ideas.

- Think of as many ideas as possible during the session—the idea list can be shortened at a later time.

- Look for combinations of ideas that might go together.

Everyone should be encouraged to contribute ideas on a rotational basis, although an individual may pass on his or her turn(s).

A repeat brainstorming session can be held after a couple days, in case someone thinks of other ideas after the original meeting. When the idea list is finalized, the group can go through the list together and combine ideas, or draw lines through ideas that do not seem feasible. The ideas remaining are ranked from most to least feasible to try.

*Multivoting.* Multivoting, or multiple voting, is a group decision-making technique designed to reduce a long list (suggested actions, improvement priorities, and so forth) to a shorter list. It can be used after brainstorming sessions to narrow down the list of original ideas.

*Cause-and-Effect Diagrams.* This tool, also called a fishbone diagram, identifies the main factors (process inputs) contributing to a measurement to be improved and/or controlled.[11] It is often used to display the main process inputs (large bones) for a selected performance measure in order to determine the likely causes of poor or unstable performance (Figure 4–5, page 61). Brainstorming sessions involving staff who are actually involved in the day-to-day performance of the measure help to identify other minor, supporting process inputs (small bones).

In manufacturing, five process inputs are often considered to influence measurement outcomes: people (staff/employees), methods (policies and procedures), equipment, materials (supplies), and environment. In health care, a sixth process input—patients—needs to be considered. Health care is a combination of science and art. It is unlike other industries in that it cannot standardize all of its process inputs (that is, patients). Thus, at times, there is a need to adjust treatment protocols to accommodate the uniqueness of different patients. This, too, is an expected process variation amenable to measurement and improvement.

*Flowcharts, Algorithms, and Pathways.* A flowchart uses symbols and words to show the steps, sequence, and relationship of various operations involved in the performance of a function or process. An algorithm is an ordered sequence of steps or instructions—each of which depends on the outcome of the previous step or instruction—that tells how to solve a particular problem. An algorithm is specific, so there can be no doubt about what to do next, and has a finite number of steps.

A clinical pathway, or treatment regimen, is agreed to by consensus and includes all of the elements of care, regardless of the effect on patient outcomes. It is a broad perspective of care and may include tests and x-rays that do not affect patient recovery. A critical pathway, or treatment protocol, is based on a consensus of clinicians and includes only those vital components or items proven to affect patient outcomes, either by the omission or commission of the treatment or by the timing of the intervention. For performance measurement, many measures are created from points or steps in the clinical or critical pathways developed for specific patient populations (such as those with acute myocardial infarction, hip fractures, or chemotherapy).

*Control Charts.* Control charts are used to assess the stability of a particular process through the statistical analysis of variation in a measure's performance over time. Variation is expected in performance measurement data, but a control chart can identify random versus nonrandom (out of the ordinary) variation. Control charts indicate whether a process is "in statistical control" (stable with only common causes of variation) or "out of statistical control" (unstable because of variation due to special causes). A control chart is a particularly useful performance improvement tool because, under a stable process, productivity is often maximized while costs are minimized; future outcomes and costs are predictable; and predictable outcomes and costs support efficient and effective management.[12] However, being "in statistical control" does not necessarily mean that performance is acceptable. It is possible to have stable and predictable performance that is substandard.

Various statistical tests for special causes can be found in statistical process control textbooks. The Joint Commission currently uses the following three common "out of statistical control" tests:

- One data point above or below the upper or lower control limit (+3 standard deviations [SD] from the center line and –3 SD, or sigma, below the mean);

- A run of eight consecutive data points on one side of the center line (overall process mean for the control chart); and

- A trend of six consecutive data points steadily increasing or decreasing.

Measures should have a minimum of 12 to 15 data points before control charts can begin to be interpreted; the upper and lower control limits are considered trial limits until 20 to 24 data points are present. (See Chapter 5 for more information on control charts and their use with comparison data analysis, pages 90–96.)

The example shown in Figure 4–6 (below) is a control chart for one organization's perioperative complication measure. The process behind the measure appears to have changed over time, as evidenced using the first two tests discussed in this section:

Test 1   Seen at the third-to-last month displayed, it indicates that a special cause may have occurred. The special cause should be investigated and removed to prevent recurrence.

Test 2   Seen at the beginning of the chart. The organization initially had a lower complication rate, and then something appears to have

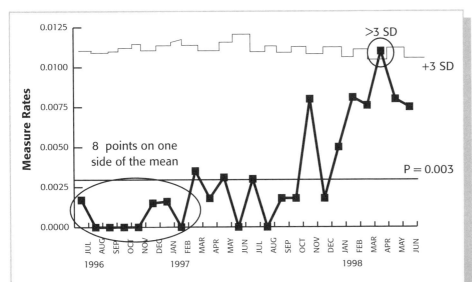

**Figure 4–6. Sample Control Chart: Perioperative Complications Within Two Days of Procedure**

This chart shows rates of perioperative complications that occur within two days of a procedure. It is possible to quantify the change in rates using two of the statistical control tests discussed in the text.

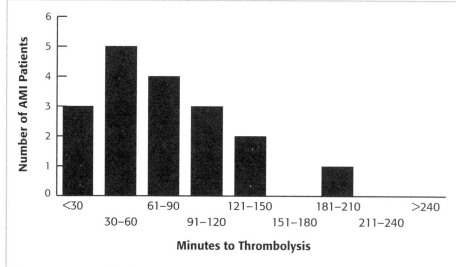

**Figure 4–7. Sample Histogram**

This figure shows the distribution of times to administration of thrombolytic therapy for acute myocardial infarction (AMI) patients at one hospital. Because the goal is to administer therapy within 30 minutes, a nonnormal distribution would be expected (skewed to the left).

changed to produce higher complication rates in the last six months or so.

Investigation into possible causes for the increased complication rates might find a data collection or quality problem for this measure that was identified and corrected midcourse, making it appear on paper that the organization had an increasing rate, when in fact the earlier low complication rates were erroneous. Alternatively, a new surgical service might have been offered midcourse and, due to its risk, higher complication rates were seen.

*Histograms.* A histogram is a vertical bar graph used to determine the shape of a data set—its dispersion, central tendency, and overall distribution. Usually the data examined using a histogram are continuous measurement values (rather than yes or no responses), so there is a wide variety of possible answers. The spread or range of the values and how frequently each occurs are of interest. The measurement values are broken up into smaller ranges on a scale from lowest to highest (Figure 4–7, above). The creator of the histogram must determine what these smaller ranges should be, although the values ideally should be divided into 7 to 20 equal subgroup ranges (depending on the number of values available).[13] A tally sheet can be used to count the number of measurement values in each subgroup range, and then the totals can be displayed in a bar graph for the histogram.

A normal distribution of data looks like the standard bell-shaped curve, where approximately 68% of the data are expected to fall between +1 and −1 SD, 95% of the data between +2 and −2 SD, and 99% of the data between +3 and −3 SD from the mean (center line of the curve). In a normal distribution, the mean, median, and mode are equal or nearly equal. Having an adequate sample size is imperative to assessing the true underlying distribution for any data set.

*Pareto Charts.* Vilfredo Pareto (1848–1923) studied the distribution of wealth in Italy and found that 20% of the population had 80% of the wealth (hence, the 80/20 rule applies to Pareto analysis). Juran popularized its application to quality to distinguish the trivial many causes of poor performance from the vital few.[14] Pareto analysis is the process of ranking opportunities to determine which should be pursued first.

When investigating special cause variation or undesirable measurement rates, drill-down analysis is performed by dividing the data into smaller subsets to help locate contributing factors (Figure 4–8, below). Several layers of drilling down often will be required in the investigational phase. Some refer to this process as "slicing and dicing" the data in different ways to get different pictures and possibly narrow down the location of the problem area. Rational subsets are the logical

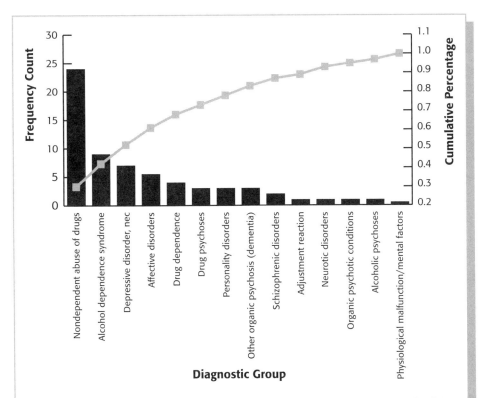

**Figure 4–8. Sample Pareto Chart: Individuals Discharged Against Clinical Advice**
This chart shows a breakout of the clinical diagnosis categories for individuals discharged against clinical advice from a behavioral health care organization's residential treatment facility. Drug- and alcohol-related conditions help contribute to the common factors of these discharges. Improvement strategies to decrease the rate of premature discharges might concentrate on this group of individuals first. This Pareto chart has a second y-axis on the right side of the chart for the cumulative percentage line, which helps the user focus on the "vital few causes" influencing the premature discharges.

groupings used to divide the data for further study and investigation of causal factors. Examples of rational subsets include the following:

- *For acute care*—Different nursing units, day and night shifts, weekends/holidays and regular work week, patient populations by age, physician/surgeon groupings, and different patient classifications (such as cardiovascular, renal, or neurological);

- *For behavioral health care*—Drug/alcohol abuse or various mental illness classifications;

- *For ambulatory care*—General anesthesia or intravenous sedation;

- *For home care*—Home medical equipment, intravenous infusion therapy, home health care, personal care or hospice; and

- *For long term care*—Medicare, Medicaid, or private payers.

To further analyze data resulting from drill-down analysis, the data can be displayed in run charts, control charts, Pareto charts, line graphs, bar graphs, pie charts, and so on.

*Run Charts.* A run chart plots data points in a time sequence graphically to show whether patterns or trends can be attributed to common or special causes of variation. A run chart is less sensitive than a control chart for identifying special cause variation, but it can be a good starting point for analyzing data quickly. Using statistical probability tests, it can help identify which existing processes need improvement and can show whether an action taken to improve performance was successful (a long run length on the desirable side of the mean or existence of common cause variation after the improvement plan was initiated). Errors can come from not finding special cause variation in a run chart when it does exist, due to the fact that run charts are especially insensitive to single points that are extremely different from the rest.

Interpreting a run chart involves counting the number of runs and looking for trends in the data to identify any special causes of variation. A *run* is defined as one or more consecutive data points occurring on the same side of the center line (the median is used as the center line in the run chart). A single point on a line is not counted; multiple points occurring on the line are assigned alternately above and below the center line. A *trend* is defined as an unusually long series of incremental increases or decreases in the data points.[15] There are three tests for interpreting run charts:

- Find the appropriate maximum run length;

- Find the appropriate number of runs (within smallest-to-largest range); and

- Find the appropriate maximum consecutive increases or decreases for trending.

Any points falling outside of these testing limits indicate the presence of special cause variation.

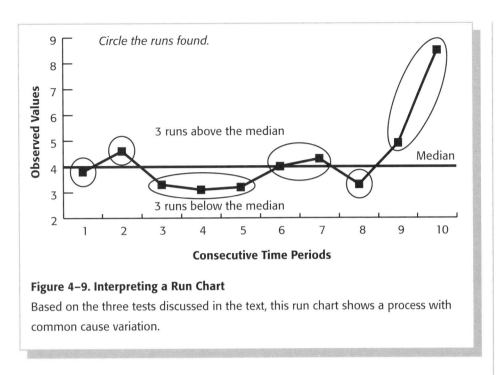

**Figure 4–9. Interpreting a Run Chart**

Based on the three tests discussed in the text, this run chart shows a process with common cause variation.

Figure 4–9 (above) shows how these tests are used. Monthly data points are plotted and connected. The median is a measure of central tendency and is the middle number when values are arranged from smallest to largest. In this example, the median falls between 5 and 6 (half of the points are above the line and half are below). The maximum run length is 5 (based on 10 data points), but 3 is the maximum here. The number of runs expected is between 3 and 8, and it is actually 6 (circled). Trend identification would occur with 5 points in a row showing an increase or a decrease, which does not happen here. The conclusion is that the variations identified are from common causes. More detailed information on the use of run charts (including the three run chart tests) may be found in *Pyzdek's Guide to SPC, Volume One: Fundamentals*[10] and in *Measuring Quality Improvement in Healthcare: A Guide to Statistical Process Control Applications.*[15]

*Scatter Diagrams.* These graphic representations of data depict the possible relationship between two variables (Figure 4–10, page 68). They show what happens to one variable when another variable changes in order to test a theory that the two variables are related. A scatter diagram cannot prove that one variable causes the other, but it does indicate whether a relationship exists and the strength of that relationship (positive, negative, or zero).

### Systems Thinking Tools

The study of systems evaluates how processes are interrelated and examines their interdependencies. Individual systems also may be interrelated, with multiple subsystems making up a larger, more complex system. The ever-changing business of health care (mergers, acquisitions, and so forth) is complex and demands better tools to monitor performance of an organization's overall delivery system.

Even in a single facility, many systems operate simultaneously and sometimes

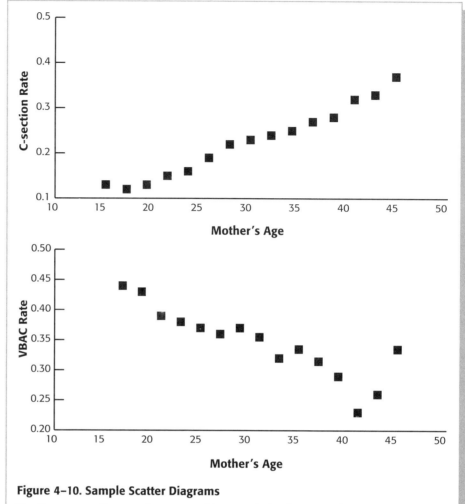

**Figure 4–10. Sample Scatter Diagrams**
The first scatter diagram shows a positive correlation between the mother's age and
the C-section rate (older mothers are more likely to have a C-section). The second
diagram shows a negative correlation between the mother's age and the rate of
vaginal birth after a C-section (VBAC).

symbiotically (such as patient assessment, patient care, and information management). Changing a policy or procedure in one system may negatively affect another system. Sometimes tradeoffs are made to give better, faster service in one system (emergency care) at the expense of another system (routine radiology services). It is crucial to monitor the impact of changes on all systems when revising processes. Two important systems thinking tools—causal loop diagrams and computer simulation—are more complex than traditional performance improvement tools.

*Causal Loop Mapping.*[8] When drawing a diagram of a system, arrows (or links) can be traced from any element (event or variable) to another, representing the first element's influence on the second. Every element has a cause and an effect, resulting eventually in a feedback loop for the system. This can result in cycles of performance that repeat themselves unless some action is taken to change the

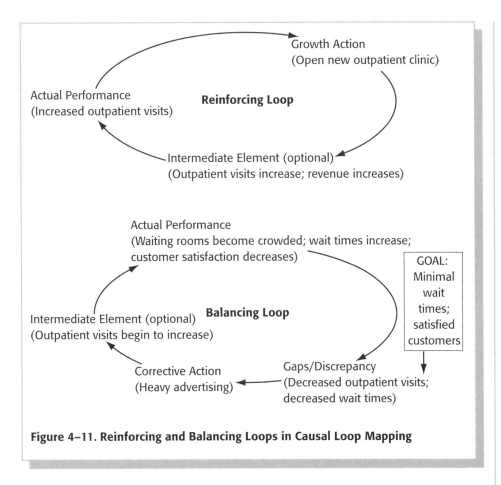

**Figure 4–11. Reinforcing and Balancing Loops in Causal Loop Mapping**

cycle. Change can also produce problems. A series of "reinforcing" loops and "balancing" loops can exist in a system.

In a reinforcing loop any number of elements can cause growth within a system. For example, a hospital may experience an increased number of outpatient visits and consider this a growth opportunity. It opens an outpatient clinic to stimulate new business. Patients begin coming to the new clinic, and revenue increases.[9]

In a balancing loop, the forces of resistance eventually limit growth. Expanding on the previous example, over time the waiting rooms become crowded, causing long wait times. Customer satisfaction, the number of visits, and wait time decrease. Corrective action is taken to fix the problem: The hospital engages in periodic heavy advertising. The number of visits increases, but so do the wait times. The short-term fix disregarded what was causing the decreased visits and introduced a repetitive balancing cycle: (advertising) visits increase, wait time increases (customer satisfaction decreases), visits decrease, wait time decreases—(advertising) visits increase, and so on. A long-term fix tries to find the right balance to keep both the number of visits and customer satisfaction at desired levels (Figure 4–11, above).[9]

*Computer Simulation.* Computer modeling is used to try out "what if" changes to a system to see whether improvements are likely to occur. One company has a Web site under the classification of "medical computer simulation." It offers software to evaluate, plan, or redesign health care systems. Computer simulation in health care is starting to become more common, with medical universities across the United States performing research in this area.

*An Integrated Example*

One 400-bed hospital received 35% of its admissions from the emergency department (ED). Both public relations and service quality problems were expressed by patients, family members, and physicians. Phase 1 of the investigational phase of the improvement process used traditional performance improvement tools. The team members developed a flowchart to better understand the situation and identified points in the process where patients might experience a wait. They limited the scope of the project to nonambulance patients (who went immediately to an ED bed without a wait). The team identified four measures to track ED wait time:

• Total patient wait time in ED (arrival to discharge, in minutes);

• Type of caregiver involved;

• Amount of time care was delivered; and

• Amount of delay patient experienced (all time patient was not receiving care, such as waiting for lab test, physician visit, or instructions).

Initial data showed frequent 3.5-hour waits (out of statistical control on a control chart), with an overall average wait time of 2 hours. A cause-and-effect diagram was created and multivoting occurred to identify the three most likely causes, which were (1) high patient arrival rates, (2) high patient acuity rates, and (3) clinic closures on weekends. Scatter diagrams were created to detect correlations between these causes and actual wait times. No significant relationship was found for any of the causes. The ED team kept diaries in an attempt to capture the special cause for the long wait times; no explanations were revealed.

Phase 2 of the investigational phase used systems thinking tools. The team decided that traditional problem-solving tools might not be appropriate if this were a systems problem. A consultant in systems thinking was asked to study whether the long waits were due to interdependencies in the ED processes. The ED staff helped to draw the complex causal loop cycles. A computer simulation of the ED care system, using much of the data collected in Phase 1, plus department staffing patterns, ED logbook data, and physical plant information about the ED, was added to the model. Simulated improvements that worked in pilot testing included computerized ordering of clinical records, creation of a direct admissions process, alerts when system conditions predicted a rise in wait times, and zone assignments (staff were assigned to specific sections of the ED).

## Training in Data Analysis

The Joint Commission's accreditation manuals include standards that apply to training in data analysis and statistical tools. Leadership standards state that an organization's leaders need to set expectations, develop plans, and manage processes to measure, assess, and improve the quality of governance, management, clinical, and support activities. Staff training in performance improvement approaches and methods is also necessary.

Improving organization performance standards state the need for leaders to establish a planned, systematic, organizationwide approach to process design and performance and that data are to be collected to monitor the stability of processes, identify opportunities for improvement, and sustain improvement. Furthermore, appropriate statistical techniques are to be used to analyze and display data. The intent of the latter requirement is that understanding statistical techniques is helpful both in assessing the nature of variation and in identifying a process that needs to be improved. By understanding the type and cause of variation through the use of statistical tools and methods, an organization can focus its attention and resources on specific areas that show room for improvement.

### Individual Training Opportunities

Individuals analyzing health care data in an organization setting may obtain training from various sources. Some learn on the job from experienced colleagues or through trial and error; others may attend workshops or other educational seminars. In addition, they may read a number of journals or books related to performance measurement and containing information about performance improvement measures and data analysis methods. They can both identify strengths and weaknesses associated with a measure's specific findings and determine whether a planned intervention is successful and the results are sustained over time. Table 4–1 (page 73) lists selected performance improvement journals and newsletters. Education and/or certification in quality management techniques is available. The following are some examples of how to become more proficient in the analysis, interpretation, and use of data:

- *Take an introductory course in statistics or statistical process control (control charts).* Most colleges offer basic statistics courses, and some even offer courses focusing on health care–related statistics. Many colleges and junior colleges offer courses in statistical process control theory, which may be found in the mathematics, business, manufacturing, or engineering sections. The basic foundation for using and interpreting control charts should be identical, regardless of the field of application, and can be adapted to health care settings with a little creativity and thought.

- *Attend educational seminars offered by national/local professional affiliations.* Many professional societies, for-profit organizations, and nonprofit organizations offer educational seminars on performance measurement in health care covering the use of performance improvement tools, including control charts and comparative data analysis.

- *Obtain certification.* The title certified professional in healthcare quality (CPHQ) is offered by the National Association for Healthcare Quality (NAHQ) to individuals who pass a written test on health care quality issues.

The CPHQ test is offered annually (in November) and tests a candidate for a comprehensive body of knowledge, including management and leadership (20%); information management (26%); education, training, and communication (12%); performance measurement and improvement (34%); and accreditation and licensure (8%). Training courses are offered by NAHQ, and a list of study materials is available at *www.cphq-hqcb.org/examin.htm*. The organization also has many affiliated state associations for local-level involvement and networking.

The American Society for Quality (ASQ) offers information related to statistical process control for the skilled quality professional, as well as for beginners. Traditionally, ASQ's focus has been on the manufacturing industry, but it has recently grown into the service industry, including health care. Among several certification programs offered by ASQ, the following two programs may be of interest to health care professionals:

- *Certified quality manager (CQM).* One of the requirements to becoming a CQM is that the candidate must have five to ten years of on-the-job experience in one or more of the following areas: quality standards, organizations and their functions, quality needs and overall strategic plans, customer satisfaction and focus, project management, continuous improvement, human resources management, and training and education.

- *Certified quality technician (CQT).* This certificate has a requirement of one to four years of on-the-job experience in one or more of the following areas: quality concepts and tools, statistical techniques, metrology and calibration, inspection and testing, quality audits, and preventive and corrective action.

Additional information on the ASQ programs can be obtained at ASQ's Web site, at *www.asq.org/standcert/certification/cqt1.html*.

## Organizational Self-Assessment Opportunities

An organization may wish to identify its strengths and weaknesses in regard to its level of organizational quality and performance or in order to showcase its efforts toward performance improvement. One way to do this is to obtain the applications and requirements for various quality awards. An organization can perform a self-assessment to determine whether it is ready to complete the application process. If it is (all the requirements are met), the organization may apply for the award as a way to reinforce and strengthen its dedication to providing high-quality services, as well as to recognize the accomplishments of its organizational team.

The Malcolm Baldrige National Quality Award is given annually to one organization in each of five categories—manufacturing, health care, service, small business, and education. Using the award criteria as a self-assessment tool has helped some organizations understand their system-level operations and educate their staff in performance improvement. These criteria also can be complemented with the ISO

**Table 4–1. A List of Some Quality Improvement Journals and Newsletters** (which have data analysis and use case studies)

| Quality Journal | Address | Web Site/E-mail Address |
|---|---|---|
| *American Journal of Medical Quality* | PO Box 1897￼ Lawrence, KS 66044 | *www.acmq.org* E-mail: *mequ@allenpress.com* |
| *Health Care Division Newsletter* | American Society for Quality 611 E. Wisconsin Ave PO Box 3005 Milwaukee, WI 53201-3005 | *www.healthcare.org* and *www.asq.org* |
| *The Inside Perspective* (Occasionally has ORYX-related articles) | Joint Commission One Renaissance Blvd Oakbrook Terrace, IL 60181 | *www.jcaho.org* |
| *International Journal for Quality in Health Care* | Journals Marketing Oxford University Press 2001 Evans Road Cary, NC 27513 | E-mail: *jnlorders@oup-usa.org* |
| *Joint Commission Benchmark* | Joint Commission One Renaissance Blvd Oakbrook Terrace, IL 60181 | *www.jcaho.org/edu_pub/ benchmrk/benchmrk.html* |
| *Joint Commission Journal on Quality Improvement* | Joint Commission One Renaissance Blvd Oakbrook Terrace, IL 60181 | *www.jcaho.org/edu_pub/ persp/pe_frm.html* |
| *Joint Commission Perspectives* (Occasionally has ORYX-related articles) | Joint Commission One Renaissance Blvd Oakbrook Terrace, IL 60181 | *www.jcaho.org/edu_pub/ persp/pe_frm.html* |
| *Journal for Healthcare Quality* | NAHQ 4700 W. Lake Ave Glenview, IL 60025-1485 | *www.nahq.org* E-mail: *info@nahq.org* |
| *Journal of Clinical Outcomes Management* | Turner White Communications, Inc 125 Strafford Ave, Suite 220 Wayne, PA 19087-3391 | *www.turner-white.com* |
| *Medical Care* | 12107 Insurance Way Hagerstown, MD 21770 | *www.medicalcare.org* |
| *Quality Digest* (Occasionally has health care–related articles) | QCI International 40 Declaration Drive Suite 100 Chico, CA 95973 | *www.qualitydigest.com* E-mail: *qualitydigest@ qualitydigest.com* |
| *Quality in Health Care* | BMJ Publishing Group PO Box 590A Kennebunkport, ME 04046 | *www.qualityhealthcare.com* and *www.bmj.com/bmj* |
| *Quality Management in Health Care* | Fulfillment, Aspen Publishers, Inc 7201 McKinney Circle Frederick, MD 21704 | *www.aspenpublishers.com* |
| *The Systems Thinker* (Occasionally has health care–related articles tied to systems thinking approaches) | Pegasus Communications, Inc One Moody Street Waltham, MA 02154-5339 | *www.pegasuscom.com* |

9000 series of quality management standards (originally developed for manufacturing) and Joint Commission standards to synergistically assist organizations in achieving excellence.[16,17] Seven categories make up the Baldrige criteria, which can be used as a framework that any organization can use to improve overall performance[18]:

- *Leadership.* Examines how senior executives guide the organization and how the organization addresses its responsibilities to the public and practices good citizenship.

- *Strategic planning.* Examines how the organization sets strategic directions and how it determines key action plans.

- *Customer and market focus.* Examines how the organization determines requirements and expectations of customers and markets.

- *Information and analysis.* Examines the management, effective use, and analysis of data and information to support key organization processes and the organization's performance management system.

- *Human resources focus.* Examines how the organization enables its workforce to develop its full potential and how the workforce is aligned with the organization's objectives.

- *Process management.* Examines aspects of how key delivery and support processes are designed, managed, and improved.

- *Business results.* Examines the organization's performance and improvement in its key business areas: customer satisfaction, financial and marketplace performance, human resources, supplier and partner performance, and operational performance (care delivery). This category also examines how the organization performs relative to competitors.

Table 4–2 (page 75) gives an overview of the Baldrige requirements specific to health care organizations, which may also consider applying for state and quality awards and/or the Ernest A. Codman Award, which is a Joint Commission award presented to organizations and individuals for exemplary achievement in the use of process and outcome measures to improve organization performance and quality of care.

## Summary

A health care organization whose leaders and staff are trained in proper performance measurement management techniques will be able to make data-driven decisions to improve performance and provide better-quality care to patients. Organizations can share their success stories and lessons learned through networking, professional associations, or publications, enabling other organizations to improve their systems as well.

**Table 4–2. Malcolm Baldrige National Quality Award's Organizational Overview for Health Care***

### Basic Description

- Nature of your health care services
- Size and location of organization and information on ownership
- Organizational culture—Purpose, vision, mission, values, as appropriate
- Major health care markets: local, regional, national, or international
- Principal customer types: patients, specific third-party payers, local community, and so forth
- Your staff: number, educational level, workforce and job diversity, bargaining units, and special safety requirements
- Regulatory environment affecting you relative to health care service delivery, occupational health and safety, environmental and financial requirements, and so forth

### Subunit Issues (if applicable)

- Organizational relationship to the parent and percentage of staff the subunit represents
- How your services relate to those of the parent and/or other units of the parent
- Key support services, if any, provided by the parent

### Patient/Customer and Health Care Market Requirements

- Key patient/customer and market requirements (such as accessibility, continuity of care, and billing requirements) for health care services
- Description of all important requirements, noting significant differences, if any, in requirements among patient/customer groups and/or market segments
- Special relationships/partnerships, if any, with customers or customer groups

### Supplier and Partnering Relationships

- Types and numbers of suppliers of goods and services
- Most important suppliers and partners
- Any limitations, special relationships, or special requirements that may exist with some or all suppliers/partners

### Competitive Situation

- Numbers/types of competitors and key collaborators
- Your position (relative size, growth) in the health care industry
- Principal factors that determine your competitive success, such as accessibility, health care and administrative support services offered, and cost
- Changes taking place that affect competition and/or collaboration

### Business Directions (as appropriate)

- New thrusts/changes in health care services or entry into new health care markets or segments
- New business alliances with suppliers, health care providers, or others
- Introduction of new technologies
- Changes in strategy
- Unique factors

*Adapted from *www.quality.nist.gov/word.docs/overview* requirements for Web.doc, April 12, 2000.

## References

1. Kaplan RS, Norton DP: The balanced scorecard—Measures that drive performance. *Harvard Business Review* 70(1):71–79, 1992.

2. Solbery L, Mosser G, McDonald S: The three faces of performance measurement: Improvement, accountability, and research. *Joint Commission Journal on Quality Improvement* 23(3):135–147, 1997.

3. Statistics Division, American Society for Quality: *ASQ Statistics Division Newsletter* 19(1):2–4, 2000.

4. O'Malley S: Systems thinking applications in healthcare: A tool for optimizing change. *The Quality Letter* 8(9):2–11, 1996.

5. Labovitz G, Rosansky V: *The Power of Alignment: How Great Companies Stay Centered and Accomplish Extraordinary Things*. New York: John Wiley & Sons, 1997.

6. Stroh P: The systems orientation: From curiosity to courage. *The Systems Thinker* 5(9):7, 1994.

7. Labovitz G: *Systems Thinking*. Presented at "A Systems Approach to Healthcare Evaluation: Setting the Course for 2000." Jan 7, 2000, Chicago.

8. Senge P: *The Fifth Discipline: The Art and Practice of the Learning Organization*. New York: Currency Doubleday, 1990.

9. Senge P, et al: *The Fifth Discipline Fieldbook: Strategies and Tools for Building a Learning Organization*. New York: Currency Doubleday, 1994.

10. Pyzdek T: *Pyzdek's Guide to SPC, Volume I: Fundamentals*. Tucson, AZ: Quality Publishing, 1998.

11. Ishikawa K: *Guide to Quality Control*. New York: Quality Publications, 1971.

12. Gitlow H, et al: *Tools and Methods of Quality*. Homewood, IL: Irwin, 1989.

13. Pyzdek T: *Pyzdek's Guide to SPC*. Tucson, AZ: Quality Publishing, 1998.

14. Ott E, Schilling E: *Process Quality Control*. New York: McGraw-Hill, 1990.

15. Carey R, Lloyd R: *Measuring Quality Improvement in Health Care: A Guide to Statistical Process Control Applications*. New York: Quality Resources, 1995.

16. Schyve P: A trio for quality: Accreditation, Baldrige and ISO 9000 can play a role in reducing medical errors. *Quality Progress* 33(6):54, 2000.

17. Joint Commission: *Assess for Success: Achieving Excellence with Joint Commission Standards and Baldrige Criteria*, 2nd ed. Oakbrook Terrace, IL, 1999.

18. www.quality.nist.gov/bcpg.pdf.htm#healthcare; Nov 29, 2000.

# CHAPTER 5:

# Statistical Analysis of Performance Measurement Data

Christine McGreevey, RN, MS
Associate Project Director
Division of Research
Joint Commission on Accreditation of Healthcare
Organizations
Oakbrook Terrace, Illinois

Kwan Y. Lee, PhD, SM
Project Director
Division of Research
Joint Commission on Accreditation of Healthcare
Organizations
Oakbrook Terrace, Illinois

The mere mention of statistics often has people saying, "I can't do that." This chapter seeks to dispel some of the anxiety associated with the subject. It first covers some basic statistical concepts used in exploratory data analysis with which most readers will be familiar. Then it introduces some more complex concepts that can be useful in evaluating performance. An organization's performance can be evaluated both for internal comparisons over time and for external comparisons to other organizations, to benchmarks, or to target performance levels.

## Using Statistics for Exploratory Analysis

Data management includes collecting needed data and ensuring their quality for credible data analysis. Rather than rely on intuition or hunches, proper data analysis allows for data-driven decision making. Data analysis and report development are key components of data management. A fundamental knowledge of basic statistics is needed to begin analyzing data, including understanding the type of measurement data collected, the underlying data distributions, the use of the measures of central tendency, and how variation is measured by the range or standard deviation of the data.

### Types of Measurement Data

As a first step, the type of data and corresponding evaluation methods required need to be determined. Measurements can be in the form of attributes or continuous data.

*Attributes Data.* A limited number of possible results exist for these data, such as the following yes/no types of measures: Patient had a Cesarean section (C-section) delivery/patient did not have a C-section delivery; patient lived/patient expired; and patient acquired a pressure ulcer/patient did not acquire a pressure ulcer. Attributes data are also referred to as "count data" because the number of individuals who experienced the attribute of interest are counted from all those who had the potential to experience the event of interest. Because the results have limited possibilities or categories, the range is limited to the number or percentage in each category. Attributes data can be evaluated using a bar chart or frequency table, as shown in Figure 5–1 (below). The variability of the results or outcomes can be estimated using the number of observations to calculate a standard deviation.

*Continuous Data.* Many possible results exist for continuous data, such as length of stay, minutes to treatment, and so on. This type of data is also called "variables data" because the results or outcomes can be indefinite on a numerical scale. Evaluation of the data includes examining the variability of the results or

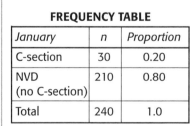

**FREQUENCY TABLE**

| January | n | Proportion |
|---|---|---|
| C-section | 30 | 0.20 |
| NVD (no C-section) | 210 | 0.80 |
| Total | 240 | 1.0 |

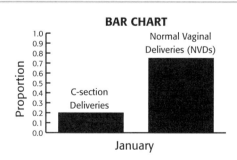

**BAR CHART**

**Figure 5–1. Analysis of Attributes Data, by Frequency Table and by Bar Chart**
Attributes data are also known as "binary" or "discrete" data because of their finite nature. Results from attributes data collection can be effectively shown in a tabular or bar chart format for interpretation.

outcomes, using the frequency distribution (histogram); the mean, median, and mode (measures of central tendencies); and the standard deviation and range.

## Data Distribution

Histograms are used to display continuous data—data tallied and reported on a numerical scale, such as average length of stay, average time to first dose of an antibiotic, average cost, and so forth. A histogram is not typically used for attributes data for which only two possible outcomes exist. Continuous data can have an indefinite number of potential outcomes (2 minutes, 35 minutes, 359 minutes, and so forth). A histogram can determine the spread of the data (range) and which outcomes are most common. Its main use is to determine whether the data are normally distributed (in a standard bell-shaped curve), skewed to the left or right, or bimodal (with two "humps," or bell-shaped curves). For normally distributed data, a bell-shaped curve is expected on the histogram (Figure 5–2, below).

The center of the bell curve is the mean, or average, of the data set. A good example is when teachers examine students' test grades to see whether they fit the standard curve. Some teachers would "grade on the curve" so more students received As, Bs, or Cs when the data were skewed to the D and F side. For normally distributed data, 68.2% of grades would be expected to fall between +1 and –1 standard deviation (or "sigma," in reference to the standard deviation of the process)[1] from the mean, 95.4% would fall between +2 and –2 sigma, and 99.8% would fall between +3 and –3 sigma. If the plotted data do not make a bell-shaped curve, the data may be too few in number (small $n$) or they may be skewed to one side (test was too easy or too hard).

Continuous measurement data can be tightly distributed (tall, narrow bell curve), with all the data points close to the mean or average, or loosely distributed (flat, wide bell curve) over a wide range of measurement values. The histogram reveals

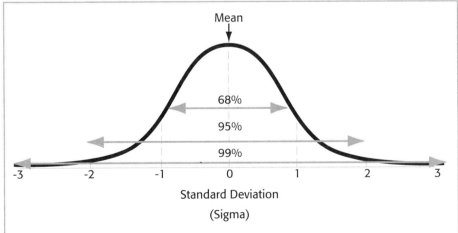

**Figure 5–2. Standard Normal Distribution (Bell Curve)**
In a normal data distribution, the mean, median, and mode are equal or nearly equal, resulting in a histogram whose highest point is in the middle, with equally sloping sides. This is called a standard bell curve.

**Group Activities for Teaching Statistics**

A plethora of books on the market purport to make nearly every subject under the sun easy to understand, but one for statistics is curiously missing. Despite this lack, there are some interesting and enjoyable activities for introducing statistical concepts to nonstatisticians,[2] including health care workers and those directly involved with quality activities in health care organizations. Rather than long lectures, interactive training is recommended. One activity for creating a bar chart involves the use of chocolate-covered candies, and another involves measuring everyone's head circumference to create a histogram. These exercises can work both as ice breakers and as a way to make the group more at ease with some of the more theoretical statistical concepts that build on the basics.

*Activity 1: Bar and Pareto Charts*

1. A plain bag of chocolate-covered candies is given to each participant, who counts the number of candies in his or her bag by color.

2. This information is tabulated on a flip chart or an overhead transparency.

3. Volunteers are asked to calculate the totals for each color.

4. The percentages for each color are calculated and used to create a bar chart (Figure 5a, page 83).

5. Each color can be thought of as a different "underlying causal factor" to some problem, and the color percentages can be sorted from highest to lowest for a Pareto chart (Figure 5b, page 83).

*Activity 2: Head Circumference Histogram*

1. Each participant measures the circumference of his or her head to the closest half inch, using an inexpensive tape measure.

2. A graph is drawn on a flip chart or an overhead transparency, with head sizes along the x-axis (from smallest to largest) and counts or number of people along the y-axis. The circumferences are tallied by marking an *X* above the appropriate measurement on the x-axis. To obtain the counts for the y-axis, the number of *X*s above each size are added together (Figure 5c, page 84).

3. A more official-looking histogram/bar graph can then be created (Figure 5d, page 84).

4. Participants are asked what they think about the underlying distribution of their data. If more heads were measured, would the data better fit the normal distribution pattern (which is fairly visible in this example with $n = 47$ heads)? Note that the range of head circumferences is from 19 to 25 inches in this data set.

the dispersion or spread of the measurement data (range from the least to the greatest measurement value) and, as such, is a form of exploratory analysis.

## Measures of Central Tendency

The mean, median, and mode are commonly used measures of central tendency in exploratory data analysis. Their definitions are as follows:

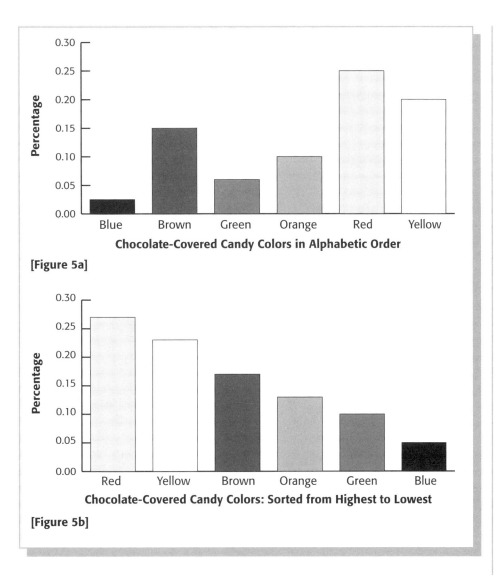

[Figure 5a]

[Figure 5b]

- *Mean* is the simple mathematical average; equal to the sum of the individual measurement values (or observations) divided by the number of observations.

- *Median* is the value in a group of ranked measurement values (or observations) that divides data into two equal parts. The median is found by sorting the measurement values from lowest to highest (or highest to lowest) and then selecting the middle observation if the number of observations is an odd number. For an even number of observations, the two middle observations are selected and the average of those two values is used for the median.

- *Mode* is the measurement value that most frequently occurs in a data set.

In normally distributed data, the mean, median, and mode are all equal. When measurement data have a small number of observations (*n*), the data tend not to be normally distributed. Hence, these three measures of central tendency will likely not be equal. The degree to which they differ can be related to a small *n*, precluding meaningful statistical evaluation and/or data that are skewed to the left or

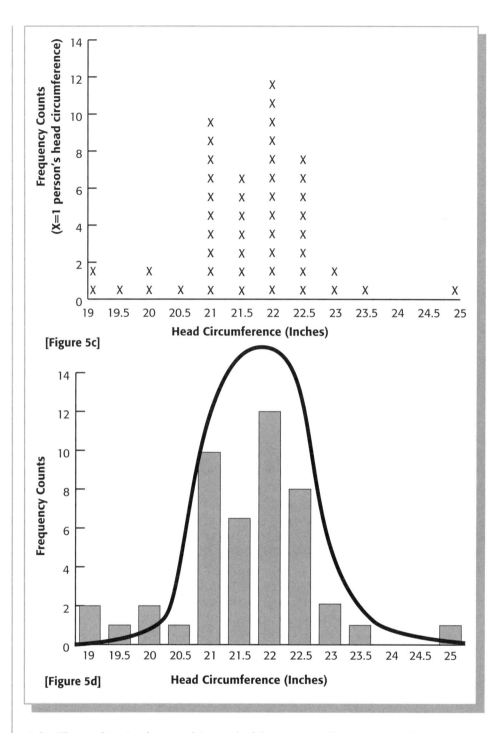

[Figure 5c]

[Figure 5d]

right. The median is often used instead of the mean as the most prominent measure of central tendency for examining measurement data having a small $n$. The mean is the most commonly used measure of central tendency.

Conventionally, run charts typically use the median as the center line, whereas control charts always use the mean. This determination is due, in part, to the run chart's use as a quick look at data; it uses the median, which is easy to determine without any calculations. The control chart is used when more precision is needed in the evaluation of the data, and it requires more complex calculations (the mean, standard deviation, and upper and lower control limits).

*Variation and Standard Deviation*

Histograms show the range of variation of the observed measurement data. Standard deviation is a measure of variability that indicates the dispersion, spread, or variation in a distribution. It is a more exact measure of variability than the range:

- *Range* is the difference between the largest and the smallest observations.

- *Standard deviation* is the amount of variability or spread about the mean. It is equal to the square root of the variance, which measures the average squared distance from the mean.

The statistical formula for calculating the standard deviation for continuous data looks complex, but is fairly easy to understand when it is broken down (Figure 5–3, page 86).

## Using Statistics for Performance Evaluation

After summarizing data from exploratory analysis of the underlying data distribution (using measures of central tendency for continuous data) and the amount of variation (bar chart or histogram), data for performance measures need to be analyzed for their stability and level of performance. Further statistical analyses important to performance measurement use run charts and control charts to evaluate whether an organization's performance is stable or unstable, and they use comparison analysis to evaluate the level of performance. Control charts and run charts (summarized in Chapter 4; see pages 62–64 and 66–67) evaluate an organization's observed performance over time to determine the overall mean (average level of organization performance). Comparison analysis is a necessary adjunct to run charts and control charts because it tells whether an organization's level of performance is similar to or different from that of other organizations, and because it is possible to provide a substandard level of care consistently (that is, stable process on control chart, but poor comparative performance).

*Analysis with Graphs and Charts*

A single measurement value has little meaning unless it can be (1) compared to some other referenced number for evaluation, or (2) evaluated with successive measurement values to study performance patterns and trends over time. Comparison data are not always readily available, and if an organization's results are unstable from one time period to another, comparisons may be meaningless. In evaluating measurement changes over time, organizations can use simple line graphs and run charts, and more complex control charts to look for trends and patterns indicative of unstable performance (also referred to as nonrandom variability, special cause variation, or signals that are out of statistical control).

Anyone who has bought a house has heard the real estate industry's mantra "location, location, location." In statistical analysis, "presentation, presentation, presentation" is a key part of data interpretation and use. Data presentation

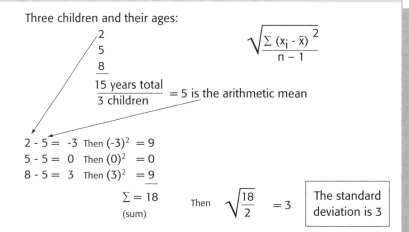

This is the formula for standard deviation for continuous data. It is not so threatening when examined step by step:

1. Look under the square root sign. The top part of the fraction begins with a Greek letter (looks like a funny E) that is the symbol for sigma, or "sum of." The sum of each result within the parentheses squared is required.

2. In the parentheses is Xi, which refers to each individual measurement (X). The data to the left are three children's ages. Each child's age is represented as an X.

3. $\bar{X}$ (X-bar) is the symbol for the average or mean of all the Xs, which is 5 in this example (15 years ÷ 3 children = 5).

4. The formula in the parentheses says to
   a. subtract the average age (X) from each of the children's ages, and
   b. square the results for each child (to obtain all positive numbers).

5. Sum, or add, all three results.

6. Divide the total by the number of children minus 1 (or 3 − 1 = 2).

7. Because the results were squared in an earlier step, it is now necessary to find the square root of the number obtained in step 6 (the standard deviation is 3).

This is a very small set of data. Just by looking at the data, it is easy to see that there are three years between each child's age. But with this formula, that variation can be calculated statistically.

Notes:

The children's ages *range* from two to eight years, which is a measure of variability or dispersion.

Their average age is 5 ± 3 (plus or minus three years, which is one standard deviation from the mean), which is a more specific measure of variability or dispersion.

**Figure 5–3. Calculating Standard Deviation for Continuous Data**

This step-by-step approach makes the formula for calculating standard deviations easier to understand and use.

involves deciding on the best display format so the data tell their own story and are readily usable and interpretable by those who make decisions and monitor performance progress. Ideally, graphically displayed data, with adequate titles and labels, should require no textual explanation.

*Bar Charts and Line Graphs.* Bar charts are helpful when evaluating category data such as the number of individuals served in a group home who suffered infections as categorized or grouped into ear infections, conjunctivitis, or urinary tract infections. For time-ordered data, however, bar charts may not be the best choice. For example, Figures 5–4 to 5–6 show the number of monthly referral calls received by an organization during 1999 and the first half of 2000. In Figure 5–4 (below), it appears that more calls were received each month in the first half of 2000 than in the same months of 1999, but any trends or patterns are difficult to distinguish. Looking at the same data in a time-ordered display in Figure 5–5 (page 88), it appears that the number of calls actually began increasing in March 2000. The line graph format in Figure 5–6 (page 88) makes this trend even more visually apparent. Stock market data are commonly presented in line graphs to show valuation trends over time for a particular stock. Some fluctuation is expected, but any peaks or valleys in the graph are studied for causative factors.

*Run Charts.* The line graph in Figure 5–6 can easily be transformed into a run chart by drawing in the median measurement value as the center line. Because there is an even number of data points (18 months), the median will lie between the ninth and tenth data points when each measurement value is sorted from lowest to highest (or highest to lowest). Rather than sort each data point, a ruler or blank piece of paper may be placed across the graph and gradually lowered from the top until nine data points are visible. The tenth data point is then determined, and the center line is drawn.

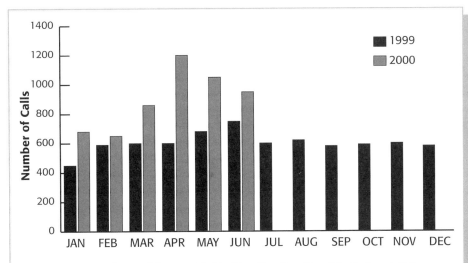

**Figure 5–4. Bar Chart with Data Divided by Months: Monthly Referral Calls Received**

It is difficult to see any trends in this data presentation, other than the fact that more referral calls were received in the first six months of 2000 than in the corresponding months in 1999.

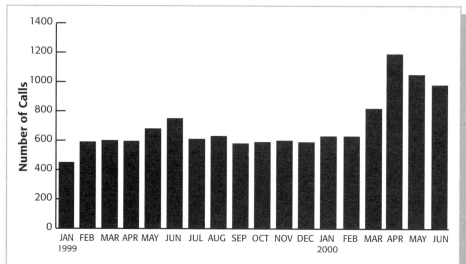

**Figure 5–5. Bar Chart with Data in Time Order: Monthly Referral Calls Received**
By displaying the data from Figure 5–4 in sequential order, it is possible to see increases, decreases, and plateaus in the number of referral calls received.

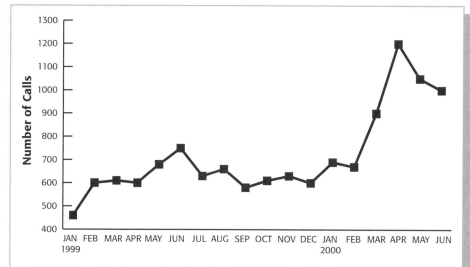

**Figure 5–6. Line Graph of Referral Call Data: Monthly Referral Calls Received**
This graph shows the trend toward an increase in monthly referral calls more clearly than either of the bar charts in Figures 5–4 and 5–5. It also may serve as the basis for a run chart.

Interpretation of the run chart to determine whether special cause variation exists involves first circling the number of runs on each side of the center line. Chapter 4 gives three run chart tests that can help determine whether the variation in the time-ordered data points is indicative of common causes or a special cause(s); see page 66. Figure 5–7 (page 89) uses these tests to look for common cause or special cause variation in the current example of monthly referral calls. All three tests demonstrate common cause rather than special cause variation. Note that if the next data point (July 2000) is above the center line, then the first test will signal special cause variation. If, however, the July 2000 data point is below the center

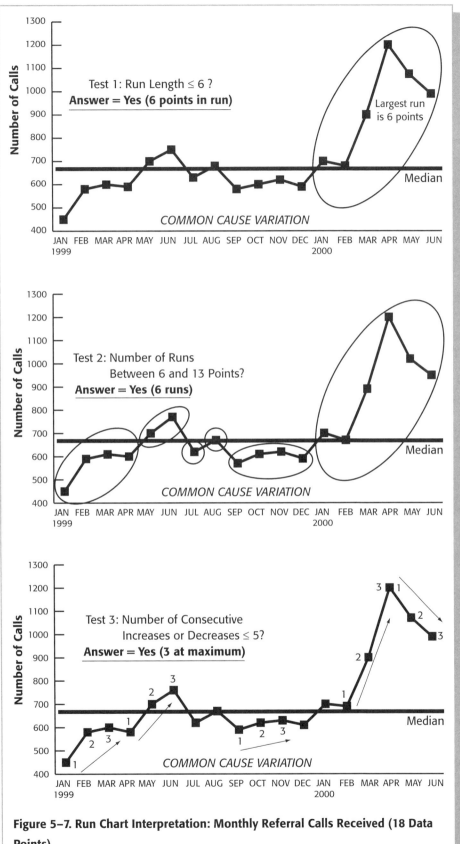

**Figure 5–7. Run Chart Interpretation: Monthly Referral Calls Received (18 Data Points)**

The line graph from Figure 5–6 is turned into a run chart by drawing in the median line. Using the three run chart tests described in Chapter 4, the variations in these

line, the second test will signal special cause variation. So, statistically speaking, this run chart is close to demonstrating special cause variation and visually, a definite increase in the number of calls can be seen during the last six months.

A shortcoming of run charts is that they are insensitive to extreme values that lie far above or below the center line. This is demonstrated by the April 2000 data point, where a two-fold increase of 1,200 calls was received as compared to the median value of about 600 calls. Distinguishing common cause from special cause variation in a run chart requires thoughtful evaluation of measurement values that are extremely different from other data points.

*Control Charts.* As mentioned in Chapter 4, control charts, like run charts, are used to assess the stability of a particular process through the analysis of performance variation for a measure over time. They indicate whether a process or an outcome is in statistical control (stable with only common cause variation) or out of statistical control (unstable with special cause variation). Control charts are also called "Shewhart charts," after Walter Shewhart, who first developed statistical process control (SPC) for manufacturing in the 1920s with the goals of meeting or exceeding customer expectations, decreasing process variation, and increasing productivity. Shewhart is also the originator of the Plan-Do-Check-Act (PDCA) process improvement cycle, which was designed to work in conjunction with control charts.

Variation exists in all human endeavors, but whether the variation is due to common causes or a special cause indicates the necessary response—either a process redesign or an investigation to remove a unique causal factor, respectively. For example, an organization decides to monitor fall rates to determine whether its fall prevention protocols are working as designed. Suppose that the organization's number of patient falls averaged 20 per month and ranged between 17 and 23 per month in a single year. This would suggest a stable process because the variation was predictable within given limits. In SPC terminology, this type of variation is said to be due to common causes. Common cause variation does not imply that the process is functioning at either a desirable or an undesirable level; it only describes the nature of variation—that it is stable and predictable within given limits or that it is in statistical control.

Now suppose that, during the following year, the organization saw the average number of falls stay the same, but in one month there were 35 falls. This change in variation would be due to a special cause. With the presence of special cause variation, a process is considered to be out of statistical control, unstable, and no longer predictable within limits. In this case, the special cause would be a negative or an undesirable finding. The organization should not make any change in its processes (its fall prevention protocols) until the special cause is identified and eliminated.

When the observed variation is due only to common causes (as in the first example), it would be appropriate to try to improve the process by introducing a new or modified process. For example, the organization might implement a fall prevention program that incorporated changes to some or all of the five common process inputs (employees, equipment, environment, supplies, and policies/procedures) of the cause-and-effect diagram. If the number of falls in the second year decreased to an average of 17 per month, with a range of 14 to 19, after introducing the prevention program, this change would be a special cause that was positive or desirable. The special cause seen on the control chart would signal the success of the intervention.[3]

In control charts, the boundary lines are called the *upper control limit* (UCL) and *lower control limit* (LCL). They are calculated by multiplying the standard deviation by three and adding it to (UCL) and subtracting it from (LCL) the mean (center line). Control charts having fewer than 25 data points (subgroups) are considered to have trial limits (UCL and LCL lines) until at least 25 data points are obtained.[4] "The determination of the minimum number of subgroups required before control limits are calculated is a compromise between a desire to obtain the guidance given by averages and control limits as soon as possible after the start of collecting data and a desire that the guidance be as reliable as possible." This leads to the policy of making preliminary calculations of control limits from the first eight to ten subgroups, with subsequent modification of limits as more subgroups are obtained.[5]

*Choosing the Right Control Chart.* There are many different control chart types. Selecting the correct control chart for the type of data collected makes interpretation more sensitive for detecting special cause variation. Performance measures are generally calculated as proportions (rates), ratios, and means (continuous data), and this information forms the basis for selecting the correct control chart. In addition, both the average rate (p-bar or u-bar/center line) for rare event attributes measures and the average number of observations (n-bar) for all type of measures need to be considered when selecting the correct chart. Table 5–1 (page 92) identifies the four common types of control charts: p-charts, u-charts, X-bar S charts, and XmR charts.

Figure 5–8 (page 93) shows examples of the four types of control charts. The p-chart and u-chart are singular charts, and the X-bar S chart and XmR charts are paired charts. To correctly interpret the X-bar and S charts, one must first interpret the S chart (which represents the standard deviation of the patient-level data each month) using only Shewhart's test for a data point beyond 3 standard deviations from the mean (UCL or LCL). If the S chart is in control, interpret the X-bar chart (which represents the standard deviation across the monthly data points) using all the tests for special causes. If the S chart is out of control, there is no point in trying to interpret the X-bar chart because it would be invalid. The special cause in the S chart should be investigated and removed.

The XmR chart (also called the individual's chart) is the control chart of choice when the number of cases each month is equal to 1. It is a paired chart (like the X-bar S chart); the first chart is the X chart and the second is the mR chart. The mR chart is calculated, beginning at the second data point, by subtracting the month from its previous month. This difference is plotted using its absolute value (a

**ORYX Tip: Control Charts**

The Joint Commission waits until an organization has used a measure for a 12-month period before it begins control chart analysis for ORYX measures as seen on the ORYX Pre-Survey Report™ used in the survey process. Then, the upper and lower control limits are recalculated with the addition of successive monthly data points.

Note that if one or more months are missing (due to organizational error, measurement system error, or simply a lack of cases), the control chart will still be presented and interpreted as long as the measure should have been collected and transmitted, for a 12-month data collection period.

**Table 5–1. Common Control Charts**

| Control Chart Type | Calculation for the Performance Measure | Measure Examples |
|---|---|---|
| p-chart | n-bar * p-bar ≥ 5 | Acute myocardial infarction (AMI) mortality: <br> *Numerator:* AMI patients discharged with a status of "expired" <br> *Denominator:* All AMI patient discharges |
| u-chart | n-bar * u-bar ≥ 5 | Number of primary bloodstream infections (PBIs) per 1,000 central line days: <br> *Numerator:* Number of PBIs <br> *Denominator:* Total number of days a central line is in place for all patients having central lines |
| X-bar S chart | n-bar ≥ 10 | Mean (average) time to initial antibiotic administration: <br> (Sum of each patient's number of minutes between time of physician's order to initial antibiotic administration time) divided by (Total number of patients receiving initial antibiotic dose) |
| XmR chart | Single measurement | Number of referral calls per month: <br> A patient's daily temperature graph |

Numerator = top part of a fraction; denominator = bottom part of a fraction; mean = sum of all the observations divided by the number of observations.

positive number) as a moving range on the mR chart. The center line for the mR chart is the overall average of the monthly moving averages. Because the mR chart is autocorrelated (each data point is created from its previous data point), it is usually not interpreted. The X chart is interpreted in the same way as the p-chart or u-chart.

Figure 5–9 (page 94) is a control chart based on the earlier example of an organization's number of referral calls per month. The XmR chart is used for this single measurement (number of referral calls) per data point. It is one of the easiest control charts to construct and also potentially less sensitive to finding special causes than the more traditional control charts (p-chart, u-chart, X-bar S chart). That is because the XmR chart does not use the standard deviation to calculate the control limit lines as do the other charts (it is mathematically impossible to calculate the standard deviation of only one observation). Instead, it uses the average moving range of the process (subtract each month's measurement value from that of the previous month) to calculate "natural process limits." (Some SPC texts refer to the XmR chart's upper and lower limits as the upper process limit [UPL] and lower process limit [LPL] instead of upper and lower control limits.) The steps in creating an XmR chart are as follows:

1. Calculate the center line. Sum each data point's measurement value and then divide by the number of data points. This is the overall process mean for the measure.

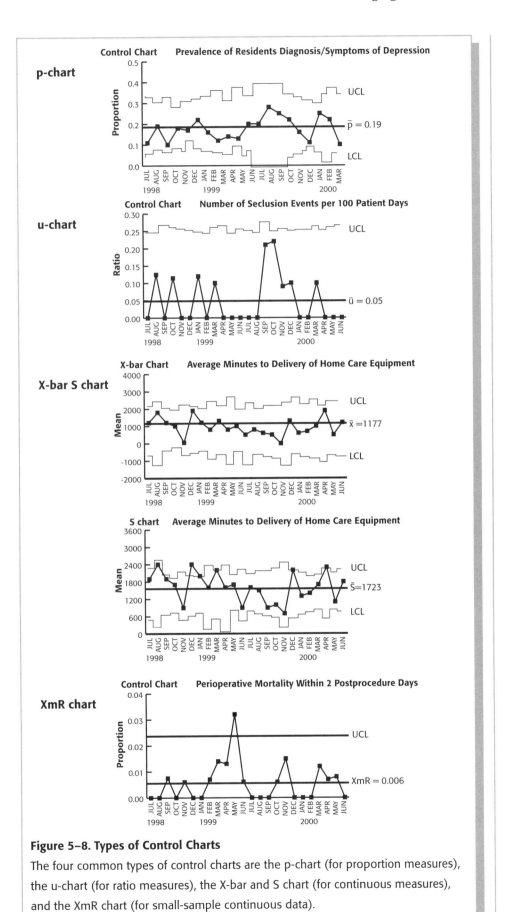

**Figure 5–8. Types of Control Charts**

The four common types of control charts are the p-chart (for proportion measures), the u-chart (for ratio measures), the X-bar and S chart (for continuous measures), and the XmR chart (for small-sample continuous data).

2. Calculate the difference between each data point's measurement value and use its absolute (positive) value, such as $|-0.05| = 0.05$.

3. Start with the second data point's value subtracted from the first data point's value—this is the moving range for data point 2 (the first data point will not have a moving range value).

4. Calculate the average moving range by summing all moving ranges and dividing by the number of moving range values (this will be one data point less than the number of data points displayed on the X chart).

5. To calculate the upper limit, take the overall process mean (center line value calculated in step 1) plus the average moving range (calculated in step 3), multiplied by 2.66.

6. To calculate the lower limit, take the overall process mean (center line value calculated in step 1) minus the average moving range (calculated in step 3), multiplied by 2.66.

7. Plot the individual data points used in step 1, the center line, and the upper and lower control limits for the X chart. Interpret using the out-of-statistical-control tests.

The XmR chart will have straight-line upper and lower control (or process) limits because they are calculated from the *average* moving range. The XmR chart may have wider control limits and may be less sensitive for detecting special cause variation than the other charts.

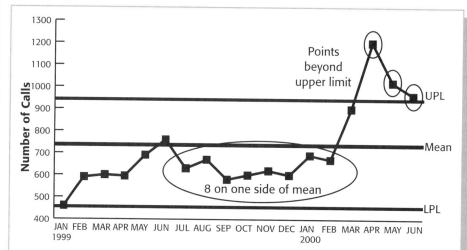

**Figure 5–9. XmR Chart Interpretation: Monthly Referral Calls Received**
This XmR chart uses the same data as Figures 5–6 and 5–7. There are several instances of special cause variation. The run of eight data points on one side of the mean suggests a process change that produced fewer calls for a significant time period. Then, the number of calls dramatically increased for three months. Investigation should occur to determine what special cause or causes contributed to the increased number of calls.

*Tests for Special Cause Variation.* Control charts are useful tools to detect special cause variation for performance improvement purposes—both to investigate problematic time periods and to affirm whether a planned improvement is having the desired effect. Shewhart used a single test to isolate data that were out of statistical control and indicative of a special cause, namely any data point beyond the upper or lower control limits. However, since Shewhart's time, other out-of-statistical-control tests have been developed. The Joint Commission, in its analysis of ORYX data, uses three tests for identifying special cause variation (Figure 5–10, below):

- Shewhart's test for a single data point beyond the upper or lower control limits (3 sigma);

- A run of eight consecutive data points on one side of the mean; and

- A trend of six consecutive data points steadily increasing or decreasing.

There are other tests for detecting special cause variation. For example, Western Electric's (now AT&T's) well-published tests include Shewhart's original test of a point beyond three standard deviations (or 3 sigma) from the mean; eight consecutive points on one side of the mean; two of three consecutive data points on the same side of the mean and beyond 2 sigma; and four of five consecutive data points on the same side of the mean and beyond 1 sigma.[6] Additional tests include 6 consecutive data points steadily increasing or decreasing, and 14 points in a row alternating up and down. These tests should be used with caution, however. Increasing the number of tests can decrease the chance of missing a special cause when it is present (Type II error), but it can increase the chance of detecting a special cause erroneously (Type I error). A type I error should not be confused with the Joint Commission's type I recommendation for insufficient or unsatisfactory standards compliance. A Type I error means that, on investigation, no justifiable reason for the special cause was found, and resources devoted to unnecessary

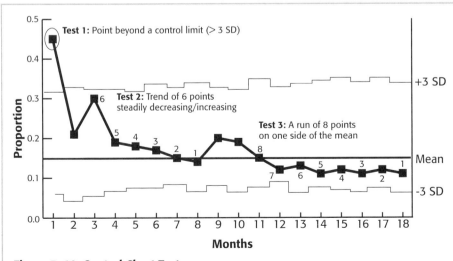

**Figure 5–10. Control Chart Tests**

The three tests described in the text are used here to identify special cause variation in the number of x-ray discrepancies found in one hospital.

investigation were potentially wasted. Using the three tests shown in Figure 5–10, a 1% chance for Type I errors exists. This means that 99% of the time, some explanation or cause should exist for special cause variation.

*Investigating Special Cause Variation.* To determine whether a special cause is a good thing to be kept or a bad thing to be eliminated depends on the context of the measure. In the previous example, if the number of referral calls is a hospital measure for community members to call in for names of physicians they can be referred to for certain diseases, this is a special cause that should probably be kept and incorporated into the organization's policies and procedures. It is likely desirable to have increased referrals to staff physicians. On the other hand, if this is a large-group practice measure, then a high rate of referrals may not be desirable, and alternatives may need to be introduced to limit the number of referrals being made (such as additional staff, better vacation coverage, a larger office environment, or purchase of needed machines/equipment).

Even if a special cause occurred some time ago, it may be worth investigating to determine what happened at that point in time so the cause can be prevented from recurring and affecting future performance. If a measure has special cause variation or if an organization is simply interested in improving its overall performance by eliminating common cause variation, the performance improvement and systems thinking tools presented in Chapter 4 can be used from this point.

## Comparison Analysis

Multiple levels of comparisons are possible and even desirable. Organizational performance can be compared to that of like organizations (those of the same size that offer the same or similar services), to organizations in the same market share location (competitors), to organizations in the same state or region, or to organizations on a national or even an international level. Many health care organizations are very interested in how their competitors are performing, because in today's world, customers can go virtually anywhere for health care—even the Web.

Comparison methodology can use the raw data from an organization's observed measurements, or it can incorporate risk-adjusted data for fairer comparisons. Not all measures require risk adjustment, but typically health outcome measures should be adjusted for each patient's severity of illness. To level the playing field in comparing outcomes, certain patient factors associated with poor outcomes should be adjusted because these factors may be beyond the control of the health care provider. Factors such as a patient's age, sex, and comorbidities are often adjusted for by

- excluding such patients from the measure to ensure a more homogeneous population (although this may lead to small sample size concerns related to data analysis);

- stratifying the measure into one or two major risk factor categories (such as age, sex, or those with diabetes and those without); or

- using statistical models (logistical regression techniques) involving multiple patient risk factors.

Some measures, such as process measures, do not require risk adjustment for fair comparisons. For example, the continuous measure that looks at the time from emergency department arrival to thrombolysis administration for acute myocardial infarction (AMI) patients having an elevated ST segment or left bundle branch block on their initial electrocardiogram is generally not risk adjusted. This process measure looks at how effective organizational policies and procedures are concerning the administration of thrombolytic medication to AMI patients who have it prescribed. It does not matter whether the patient is 35 years old or 65 years old, whether the patient is diabetic or a smoker, or has other extenuating circumstances.

### Explaining Performance Measures

People using performance measurement data should know how each measure is constructed (inclusions and exclusions); why it is important to measure; and what medical guidelines, if any, support the measure. When presenting measurement data to others, it is very important, therefore, to clearly explain what the measure is, how its population is defined, who is excluded, and whether the measure is risk adjusted. Proper explanations are imperative for the data to be used to make informed decisions.

Using the time-to-thrombolysis measure, if the AMI patient has certain characteristics or comorbidities (such as a recent surgery or cerebrovascular accident), he or she may not be eligible to receive the thrombolytic medication. If the patient is not eligible to receive thrombolytics, he or she has no time to include for this measure and is therefore excluded (this seems straightforward, but many people become confused about this point). The measure is evaluating the organization's process for deciding (1) whether the patient is having an AMI; (2) whether the patient is a candidate for thrombolysis; and (3) if the patient is a candidate, what amount of time is required to give the order and to have someone carry out the order and begin administration of the thrombolytic agent.

This measure has another confusing aspect. A common approach to comparison analysis is to compare one organization's performance to that of other organizations using the same measure, but the real target goal (according to AMI guidelines and the National Heart, Lung, and Blood Institute) is that every patient eligible to receive thrombolysis for an AMI should receive it within 30 minutes of arrival. This measure really does not need an external comparison because the target benchmark is so well defined (this is often *not* the case in health care data). Therefore, an organization that does have an average rate of 30 minutes for all patients may be giving substandard care if some AMI patients are receiving thrombolysis far longer than 30 minutes after arrival.

A poorly constructed measure can yield virtually incomparable results that, when presented, can cause unneeded alarm and possible apathy toward performance measurement for improvement purposes. An example of this is a home care (proportion) measure, with prevalence of health status being maintained or improved as defined here:

*Numerator:* All home care clients who improved or stayed the same on their recent assessment of activities of daily living (ADL) compared to their last previous assessment score.

*Denominator:* All home care clients who received an assessment for this time period (that is, current month).

*Exclusions:* None

This measure's population (denominator) includes all home care clients who received an assessment for a certain month. Of those in the denominator, how many are included in the numerator because either the client showed improvement from the last ADL assessment or the client had the same score on the last ADL assessment? This seems straightforward, until it is known that the assessments occur every 60 days, upon initial admission to home health care, or when a change in a client's health status occurs (typically a worsening condition).

Two loopholes make comparisons (both internal on the control chart and external) for this measure tricky. One is new clients and the other is clients whose health status changes, that is, worsens. The good news is that an organization in a steady state (no new admissions and no clients who suffer a negative change in health status) is in good shape. But is health care ever in a steady state? Not really. That is why this measure is setting the organization up for possible failure.

The comparison problem lies in the measure's structure. First of all, when no previous assessment exists, the client cannot be put in the numerator, so new clients penalize the home care organization. Second, when a client worsens and an assessment is done (which is certainly a correct action), the comparison from the last assessment will most likely be negative, so again the client will not be in the numerator. This last "ding" to the home care organization may be appropriate if the organization could have done something to prevent the condition causing the health status change. If the measure is risk adjusted to the patient factors, comparisons would be fairer. However, a better measure for comparison purposes might be to exclude new clients and perhaps those clients who undergo an emergency assessment due to a status change. Adding the first or both of these two simple exclusions would allow for an "apples to apples" comparison and more user acceptance for the measure's results.

### Methods of Comparison Analysis

Comparison data are commonly reported as summary data in tables as rows and columns of numbers. To make data comparisons easier to understand, the following presentation methods are often used:

- Rank order;

**Table 5–2. Prevalence of Falls: Annual Rates for Ten Nursing Homes**

| Nursing Home | Annual Fall Rate |
|---|---|
| A | 0.239 |
| B | 0.111 |
| C | 0.083 |
| D | 0.093 |
| E | 0.109 |
| F | 0.132 |
| G | 0.184 |
| H | 0.163 |
| I | 0.130 |
| J | 0.094 |
| Group average | 0.133 |

- Percentiles;

- Z-scores for outlier performance;

- Confidence intervals; and

- Various graphical displays.

For demonstration purposes, the performances of ten long term care organizations are compared for the measure prevalence of falls in Table 5–2 (above).

*Rank Order.* When objects are ranked, they are placed in the order of their relative position, which is commonly from the highest to lowest score or the best to the worst performance. For example, a high school's graduating class members are typically ranked from the student who has the highest grade point average (GPA) to the student who has the lowest. Table 5–3 (page 100) ranks the nursing homes from Table 5–2 in order of performance. In this case, the highest score is least desirable. Nursing Home C is ranked first, with the smallest rate of falls (8%), and Nursing Home A is ranked last, with the highest rate of falls (24%). When ranking objects, it is important to consider the context of the measure, or what is a desirable versus an undesirable rate.

*Percentiles.* A percentile is a numbering statistic indicating the relative position of an individual score per 100 scores, arranged in the order of magnitude. Percentiles offer another approach to quantify the spread of data in a distribution. Here, the summary rates for proportion or ratio measures from many entities are considered examples of continuous data that can be plotted as a histogram. The median data point is equal to the 50th percentile (divides the data set in half). Sometimes the spread of a distribution is characterized by specifying the 10th and 90th percentiles to remove extreme data points on either side of a distribution. Using the high school class rank example, imagine that 530 students are divided into 100 blocks with approximately 5 students in each percentile. The top five ranked students would be in the first percentile. Meghan, who ranked 30th, would be in

**Table 5–3. Rank Order for Prevalence of Fall Data**

| Rate of Falls | Nursing Home | Rank | Percentile | Quartile |
|---|---|---|---|---|
| 0.083 | C | 1 | 9th | < 25th |
| 0.091 | J | 2 | 18th | |
| 0.093 | D | 3 | 27th | 25th–49th |
| 0.109 | E | 4 | 36th | |
| 0.111 | B | 5 | 45th | |
| 0.130 | I | 6 | 55th | 50th–74th |
| 0.132 | F | 7 | 64th | |
| 0.163 | H | 8 | 73rd | |
| 0.184 | G | 9 | 82nd | ≥ 75th |
| 0.239 | A | 10 | 91st | |

the 6th percentile block of the distribution for her graduating class—meaning that 6% of the students would have a higher GPA than hers (because the GPAs are ranked from highest to lowest). Meghan's percentile rank is calculated as follows:

$$\frac{\text{Student's rank} \times 100}{\text{No. of students} + 1} = \frac{30 \times 100}{531} = 5.65, \text{ or 6th percentile}$$

Frequently used percentiles are quartiles (25th, 50th, and 75th percentiles). It is often helpful to look at the 25th to 75th quartiles (the middle half of an ordered data set, called the "interquartile range") to assess the overall spread of a distribution. Using the example of the ten nursing homes in Table 5–3, the interquartile range (25th to 75th) is 7% (9.3% to 16.3%), which can be considered the midrange for rate of falls in this group. Therefore, Nursing Homes C and J would be performing better than the middle half of nursing homes, and A and G would be performing worse. It can be said that Nursing Home A (the 91st percentile) has a rate of falls greater than or equal to 91% of the observations; therefore, it can also be said that Nursing Home A is in the bottom 9%. This is because of the order in which the nursing homes were ranked, with 1 being assigned to the nursing home that had the lowest rate of falls. When using percentiles, cautious measurement translation is required to determine which end of the percentile range is desirable.

Box plots are a type of graphical display of comparison data using the interquartile range (25th to 75th percentile). The lines extending from the box in Figure 5–11 (page 101) are equal to 1.5 times the height of the box (75th minus 25th percentile values). Any points beyond these lines are considered to be outliers, which are not

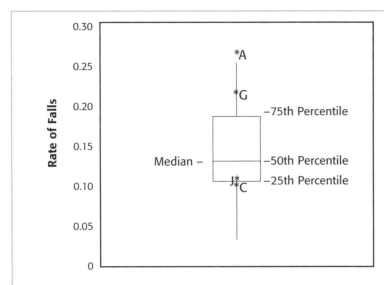

**Figure 5–11. Box Plot: Rate of Falls**

This box plot shows a comparison of the data given in Table 5–3. Nursing Homes A and G are outliers, whereas nursing homes J and C are performing better than the 25th percentile.

typical of the rest of the data. Nursing Home A is an outlier point. Also, the median line (50th percentile) is not exactly in the middle of the box (which is the middle half of the data set), indicating that the data are somewhat skewed toward the lower rates.

*Z-Scores for Outlier Performance.* At this point, it may be tempting to stop. Ranks, percentiles, and even the box plot are not too difficult to understand because they mainly involve sorting all possible measurement results from the highest to lowest (or lowest to highest) value and dividing the data into percentiles or quartile ranges. A Z-score may sound like a difficult concept, but it's not. A Z-score really tells how many standard deviations from the mean a particular measurement value or score is. Because a Z-score is based on the mean and standard deviation calculations, it can be a more precise evaluation tool for detecting outlier performance than medians and percentiles.

The Z-score is based on a standardized normal distribution where a unique measurement value, such as a health care organization's observed rate of performance, is transformed into a value that portrays where that organization's level of performance lies in relation to the overall group mean (represented as the zero value in Figure 5–12, page 102). If the organization's Z-score equals zero, its level of performance is the same as the group's level of performance. An organization having a Z-score that lies in either tail (the area approximately beyond –3 or +3 standard deviations) is considered a statistical outlier because the organization appears to be performing far better or far worse than others (depending on the direction of improvement for the measure).

Using the example of the ten nursing homes, the group average (mean) rate of falls is 13.4% and is represented as the center point (zero) on the standard bell curve. Next, each of the ten nursing homes' observed rates is similarly transformed to a Z-score value. Outlier performance is defined as performance that is statistically significantly different (either good or bad) from the average performance of others (expected performance). To be exact, a conservative measure of outlier performance uses a Z-score greater than +2.576 or less than –2.576 standard deviations from the mean (both tails of the distribution beyond 99% of the data), as shown in Figure 5–13 (below). A stricter measure of outlier performance uses a Z-score greater than +1.96 or less than –1.96 standard deviations from the mean (95% of the data).

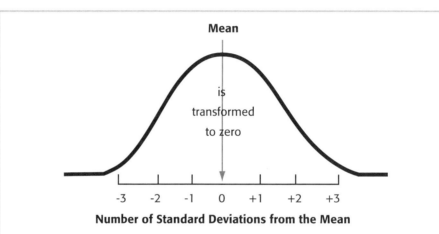

**Figure 5–12. Z-scores to Determine Outlier Status**

A Z-score shows where an organization's performance lies in relation to the performance of other organizations for the same measure. If the Z-score is zero, performance is the same as that of the rest of the group.

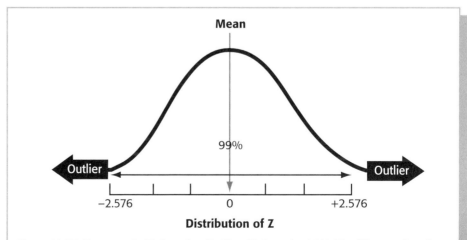

**Figure 5–13. Z-scores to Determine Outlier Status at a 99% Significance Level**

How many standard deviations from the mean is the observed value?

The following equation demonstrates how a Z-score is calculated using Nursing Home A's observed rate of falls ($n \geq 25$). An additional piece of data is necessary, namely the number of observations ($n$ in this example is the number of residents):

$$Z = \frac{\text{Observed} - \text{Expected}}{\sqrt{\dfrac{\text{Expected X } (1 - \text{Expected})}{n}}} = \frac{0.239 - 0.134}{\sqrt{\dfrac{0.134 \, x(1 - 0.134)}{200}}} = \frac{0.105}{0.024} = 4.375$$

The observed rate of falls is 0.239; the expected rate is 0.134 (the group's mean rate of falls); and $n$ is 200 residents. The Z-score of 4.375 is beyond the 2.576 mark. Nursing Home A therefore demonstrates outlier performance that is statistically different from the average performance.

For additional reference purposes, the following formula shows how to calculate a Z-score for continuous measurement data ($n \geq 10$):

$$Z = \frac{\text{Observed} - \text{Expected x } \sqrt{n}}{\text{Standard Deviation}}$$

It is similar to the previous formula, but it requires calculation of the standard deviation for the observed measurement value, as shown in Figure 5–3.

*T-statistic.* The t-statistic is a standardized score that is used in place of the Z-score for measures having a small number of observations or sample size ($n$). If Nursing Home G, for example, has only 20 residents (the measure's denominator), a t-value can be calculated and used in place of the Z-score. Whereas the Z-score is a single distribution, there are many t distributions—in fact, there is a different t distribution for different sample sizes.[7]

The formula to find the t distribution is the same as that for the Z-score, but instead of using 2.576 (for a 99% data distribution limitation) to determine outlier performance, the critical value of t is used for the appropriate degrees of freedom (df). *Degrees of freedom* is a statistical term equal to $n - 1$, or, in this example, 19 (20 residents minus 1). Many statistical textbooks include a "t distribution table" with each row equal to a particular df and columns equal to the area in one "tail" of the data distribution (Table 5–4, page 104). If three standard deviations (99%) from the mean are used as the outer boundary line, one refers to the column labeled 0.05, which is equal to the area under each tail of the distribution (that is, half of the remaining 1% of the distribution for each side).

Nursing Home G, with 20 residents, would look for the appropriate t value at the intersection of the row for 19 df and the column for 0.05. Then, it would use that number (1.729) to determine whether its calculated t value is indicative of outlier performance:

$$t = \frac{0.184 - 0.134}{\sqrt{\dfrac{0.134 \times (1 - 0.134)}{20}}} = 0.66$$

Using this formula, we can see that Nursing Home G does not demonstrate statistical outlier performance. Its calculated t value (0.66) is within the –1.729 and +1.729 boundary for this small sample size.

*Confidence Intervals.* A confidence interval establishes a range and specifies the probability that this range encompasses the true population mean. For instance, a 99% confidence interval (approximately) is calculated by taking the sample mean plus or minus 3 standard errors of the mean. The standard error of the mean is obtained by dividing the standard deviation by the square root of $n$ (number of observations). Whereas the standard deviation is used to describe the variability of the measurement values, the standard error is used to draw inferences about the

## ORYX Tip: Using Statistical Analysis Techniques

Both internal (control charts) and external (comparison charts) statistical analysis techniques are applied to ORYX performance measurement data. The ORYX Pre-Survey Report™ displays data in both formats. Although comparison analysis can be performed with only one month's data, a control chart requires a 12-month data collection period prior to analysis. Measures that a health care organization has used for less than 12 months will not have accompanying control charts in the Pre-Survey Report. If a measure was used for 12 months prior to the survey date and one or more monthly data points are missing, the control chart is generated and evaluated using only Shewhart's test for special cause variation.

Each ORYX performance measure is calculated as a proportion (rate), ratio, or continuous variable measure. The majority (80%) of the data received are for proportion measures (15% continuous variable measures; 5% for ratio measures). The statistical analyses are influenced by how the measure is defined by the performance measurement system and the monthly

**Table 5–4. Excerpt from a *t* Distribution Table**

| df | 0.05 (for 99%) |
|----|----------------|
| 1  | 6.314 |
| 2  | 2.920 |
| 3  | 2.353 |
| 4  | 2.132 |
| 5  | 2.015 |
| 6  | 1.943 |
| 7  | 1.895 |
| 8  | 1.860 |
| 9  | 1.833 |
| 10 | 1.812 |
| 11 | 1.796 |
| 12 | 1.782 |
| 13 | 1.771 |
| 14 | 1.761 |
| 15 | 1.753 |
| 16 | 1.746 |
| 17 | 1.740 |
| 18 | 1.734 |
| 19 | 1.729 |
| 20 | 1.725 |
| 21 | 1.721 |
| 22 | 1.717 |
| 23 | 1.714 |
| 24 | 1.711 |

*Source: Adapted from Pagano M, Gauvreau K: Principles of Biostatistics, 2nd edition. Brooks/Cole, an imprint of the Wadsworth Group, a division of Thomson Learning, 1994. Used with permission,*

(continued on page 105)

population from the sample that has been taken. A larger sample of observations, such as that from Nursing Home A's 200 residents, will have a smaller standard error than those with a smaller sample (that is, fewer residents).

The standard error for proportion data is calculated by taking the square root of the overall group mean multiplied by 1 minus the overall group mean divided by the number of residents in the rate of falls measure for Nursing Home A:

$$\text{Standard error (A)} = \sqrt{\frac{0.134 \times (1 - 0.134)}{200}} = 0.024$$

The standard error for proportion data is calculated similarly as Nursing Home A's, but the $n$ in the denominator is 20 for the 20 residents in the measure's denominator for Nursing Home G:

$$\text{Standard error (G)} = \sqrt{\frac{0.134 \times (1 - 0.134)}{20}} = 0.076$$

Nursing Home A's rate of falls has a standard error equal to 0.024, whereas Nursing Home G's standard error on this same measure is larger, at 0.076. This is because there is less confidence with small sample sizes. It can be said that there is 99% confidence that the true mean rate of falls for Nursing Home A should lie within the overall mean rate plus or minus 2.576 times the standard error (0.134 ± 0.062) or the confidence interval between the lower and upper confidence limits of 0.072 and 0.196, respectively. However, Nursing Home A's observed rate (0.239) does not fall within this confidence interval, and therefore would be demonstrative of outlier performance. Likewise, for Nursing Home G, there is 99% confidence that the true mean rate of falls lies within 0.134 ± 0.196 (or the confidence interval between 0 and 0.330). Nursing Home G's observed rate of falls (0.184) does fall within this generous confidence interval; therefore, its rate is not statistically significant. (By definition, a proportion measure must be between 0 and 1, so the lower confidence limit would be artificially truncated at 0 for Nursing Home G.)

With a larger number of observations, more statistical precision or power is added to data analysis—allowing for more meaningful interpretations and use of the data. Cautious interpretation of results derived from small populations is necessary to prevent erroneous conclusions being drawn. Using standard deviation and standard error, which are based on sample size calculations, helps to curtail data analysis mistakes. Figure 5–14 (page 106) shows a sample report format that uses a 95% confidence interval to present outcomes for hospitals in one state. Patients were surveyed at discharge to rate each hospital's level of performance relative to coordination of care. Each hospital was listed in alphabetic order with a black circle denoting the hospital's score and a horizontal bar indicating its confidence interval around the observed rate of performance. Two vertical bars provide comparison functionality. The first vertical bar represents the national average rate developed from national comparative databases over a rolling two-year period; the national rate was 0.71. The second vertical bar represents the state mean,

(continued from page 104)

sample size. The types of control charts used are as follows:

- *p-chart.* For proportion measures with an average number of denominator cases per month ($n$) times the overall process mean or center line ($p$) greater than or equal to 5 ($n \times p \geq 5$). Also, conversely, $n \times (1 - p) \geq 5$ needs to be true.

- *Adjusted p-chart.* For small-sample proportion measures with an average number of denominator cases per month ($n$) times the overall process mean or center line ($p$) less than 5 ($n \times p < 5$), or $n \times (1 - p) < 5$.

- *u-chart.* For ratio measures with an average number of denominator cases per month ($n$) times the overall process mean or center line ($u$) greater than or equal to 5 ($n \times u \geq 5$).

- *Adjusted u-chart.* For small-sample ratio measures with an average number of denominator cases per month ($n$) times the overall process mean or center line ($u$) less than 5 ($n \times u < 5$).

- *X-bar S chart.* For continuous measures with an average monthly number of cases ($n$) greater than or equal to 10 ($n \geq 10$).

(continued on page 106)

*(continued from page 105)*

- *XmR chart.* For continuous measures with an average monthly number of cases (*n*) less than 10 (*n* < 10).

In relation to comparison charts, Z-score calculations for observed rates greater than +2.576 and less than −2.576 (with a 99% expected confidence interval) are used for the following types of measures:

- Proportion measures having the number of denominator cases for the month greater than or equal to 25;

- Ratio measures having the number of numerator cases for the month greater than or equal to 5; and

- Continuous variable measures having the number of monthly cases greater than or equal to 10.

Similarly, t-value calculations for observed rates are used for the following types of measures:

- Small-sample proportion measures with the number of denominator cases for the month less than 25;

- Small-sample ratio measures with the number of numerator cases for the month less than 5; and

- Small-sample continuous variable measures with the number of monthly cases less than 10.

*(continued on page 107)*

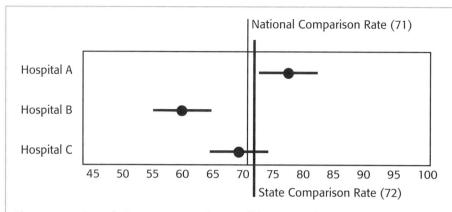

**Figure 5–14. Sample Report Format for Confidence Level Comparisons: Coordination of Care Comparisons**

The horizontal lines show the patient satisfaction rates for individual hospitals; the vertical bars indicate the national and state comparison rates. A hospital's performance is statistically significant if its horizontal line does not intersect one or both of the vertical lines.

which was calculated as the average of the performance scores of all hospitals within that state; the state's rate was 0.72. To find performance that is statistically significant on this report, one needs to look for any hospital's confidence interval (horizontal bar) that does not include either the national or state rates (cross one or both vertical bars). From this report, then, Hospital A appears to be demonstrating performance excellence, because its range of performance is beyond that of both the national and state comparison rates. Hospital B seems to be demonstrating substandard performance; its range of performance is inferior to both comparison rates. Finally, Hospital C's performance is similar to that of both the national and state averages; its range of performance coincides with these rates.[8]

*Other Graphical Displays of Comparison Data.* There are many ways to present comparison data graphically. Graphics—including bar charts, control charts, and so on (see Chapter 4)—can add more interpretive value to data than can a tabular format. Shewhart, the creator of the control chart, gave two rules for the presentation of data[9]:

- Data should always be presented in a way that preserves the evidence in the data for all the predictions that might be made from these data; and

- Whenever an average, a range, or a histogram is used to summarize data, the summary should not mislead the user into taking any action that the user would not take if the data were presented in a time series.

A combination of graphs and tables, used together in a complementary fashion, enable the user to have at hand all the available information for making

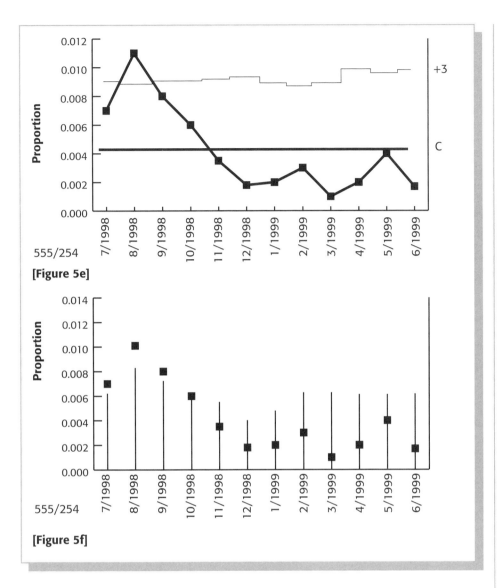

555/254
**[Figure 5e]**

555/254
**[Figure 5f]**

*(continued from page 106)*

A statistical textbook should be used to find the appropriate t-value at the 0.05 column for the appropriate degrees of freedom (df = $n - 1$; where $n$ = the number of observations for the organization's observed monthly rate).

The following figures are examples of how data might be displayed in a presurvey report for a measure whose numerator is the number of diagnostic x-rays interpreted incorrectly by nonradiologists and whose denominator is the total number of diagnostic x-rays read by nonradiologists. The control chart example (Figure 5e, left) has an upper control limit of +3 and a lower control limit of –3 (which is not shown because the lower limit cannot be less than zero for proportion measures). In the comparison chart example (Figure 5f, left), the dots represent the observed (actual) rate or value, the vertical lines are the expected range, and the horizontal dashes indicate the expected rate or value.

Using these analysis tools, it seems that, although the measure's process is unstable, a change has occurred that resulted in a lower error rate. The organization might ask itself what change(s) was implemented, whether the change(s) was implemented as part

evidenced-based decisions or for deciding whether further investigation is warranted. When presenting data for use and interpretation, users should understand

- who collected the data;

- how the data were collected;

- when the data were collected;

- where the data were collected; and

- what these values represent.

Each organization must decide which analysis and presentation styles are best suited to its information and performance improvement needs.

*(continued on page 108)*

(continued from page 107)

of policies and procedures, whether the lower rate is sustainable, and how many x-rays are actually read by nonradiologists per month. As far as process capability, the organization seems to be operating at about a 0.2% error rate and the comparison group at about a 0.3% error rate. Leaders need to decide whether they are comfortable with the current performance level or whether they should attempt to lower the error rate further. This may depend on how serious the errors have been (clinical significance issues). The number of organizations in the comparison group is also an important factor.

## Summary

Analysis of performance measurement data is a necessary part of the improvement process, and some familiarity with statistics is necessary to perform that analysis effectively. The statistical techniques used do not need to be complex to be effective, nor is great variety needed. More important is knowing how to choose the best tool to display data accurately and how to interpret it to make informed decisions about improving processes.

## References

1. Hart M, Hart R: *Quantitative Methods for Quality and Productivity Improvement*. Milwaukee: ASQC Quality Press, 1989.

2. Lackey J: Statistics for dummies: How to make SPC fun and (somewhat) easy. *Quality Progress* 31(7):112, 1998.

3. Joint Commission: *Mining ORYX Data 2000*. Oakbrook Terrace, IL, 2000.

4. Gitlow H, et al: *Tools and Methods of Quality*. Homewood, IL: Irwin, 1989.

5. Grant E, Leavenworth R: *Statistical Quality Control*, 6th ed. New York: McGraw-Hill, 1988.

6. Western Electric Company: *Statistical Quality Control Handbook*. Indianapolis: AT&T Technologies, 1982. (Originally published in 1956.)

7. Wassertheil-Smoller S: *Biostatistics and Epidemiology: A Primer for Health Professionals*. New York: Springer-Verlag, 1995.

8. Rogers G, Smith D: Reporting comparative results from hospital patient surveys. *International Journal for Quality in Health Care* 11:251–259, 1999.

9. Wheeler D: *Understanding Variation: The Key to Managing Chaos*. Knoxville, TN: SPC Press, 1993.

# CHAPTER 6

# Case Studies

The data management information presented in the first five chapters of this book is useful only if health care organizations know how to apply it effectively and integrate it into their performance improvement activities. The case studies in this chapter show how four real organizations have done just that. The projects profiled range from fairly simple to complex, and the settings include a hospital, the home health program of a skilled nursing facility, a network, and a behavioral health center.

The methods used are equally diverse, which helps to illustrate several key points made throughout this book. Parker Jewish Institute's home health program worked to improve process measures related to its intake (admissions) process. The program used basic techniques that worked well for this particular project and showed that data management does not need to be statistically complex to be effective. A large part of the improvement effort for Hazelden Center City, a behavioral health facility, addressed the data management process itself. This case study highlights the fact that staff compliance and buy-in are key to the success of data management and performance improvement. Like the other organizations profiled, South County Hospital staff identified ORYX indicators that fit with their existing performance improvement goals. They found that initial improvement can even out, and that the data collection/analysis/reporting cycle is important in

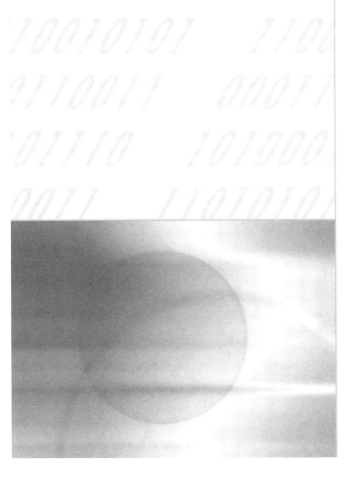

showing progress. Finally, although the volume of data involved necessarily increases when dealing with a large patient population across multiple settings, the basic tenets for managing those data are the same. The project undertaken by North Shore–Long Island Jewish Health System to reduce the number of pressure injuries among its patients illustrates that measuring both patient outcomes (level of skin care) and financial outcomes (resource utilization) is an attainable goal.

## Case Study #1: Home Care
## Parker Jewish Institute for Health Care and Rehabilitation

Parker Jewish Institute, located in New Hyde Park, New York, is a large skilled nursing and rehabilitation facility that provides inpatient and outpatient services to more than 7,000 elderly patients annually. Its home health program serves approximately 1,000 of these individuals, furnishing a wide range of individualized medical and nursing services. The program's policies and procedures say that, as part of the initial nursing assessment, patients are prioritized for therapy referrals based on the level of care needed; the time frame required for initial visits by therapists depends on the priority accorded each patient's needs. For example, priority "A" patients need a therapist visit within 48 hours of assessment, and priority "B" patients are scheduled for visits within three to five days. In all cases, the therapist is to follow up with the nurse by telephone within 24 hours of the initial visit.

### *Identifying an Opportunity for Improvement*

In 1997, as part of a routine review of clinical records, the rehabilitation supervisor realized that these requirements were not being met for all patients. Using the documentation of the nursing assessment, the initial visit, and the follow-up call in the records, she found that in the last quarter of the year only 75% of therapy visits were completed on time, and follow-up calls were made only 50% of the time. This situation provided an obvious opportunity for improvement.

An interdisciplinary performance improvement team was formed in January 1998. It comprised staff members who were involved in the assessment and referral process, including an admission assistant (responsible for completing the therapy referral), a nurse from the intake department, a nurse from the home care program, a medical scheduler (responsible for processing therapy referral paperwork), and the rehabilitation supervisor (who served as team leader). The team created a two-part opportunity statement based on the available data:

- To improve the timeliness of the initial therapy evaluation visit to comply with policies and procedures; and

- To improve the timeliness of the initial therapy evaluation telephone conference to the home care nurse manager.

The performance measures for the project thus were

- the number of visits made within the required time frame, divided by the total number of admissions; and

- the number of follow-up telephone conferences made, divided by the total number of admissions.

## Finding the Problem

To help determine where problems occurred, the team created a flowchart of the therapy referral process as it existed, from the initial nursing assessment through documentation of the initial therapy visit in the clinical record by the home care nurse manager (Figure 6–1, page 112). "By looking at the flowchart, we were able to make some 'quick fixes' that expedited the referral process to the therapists," says Stephanie Morahan, administrator of the home care program. Team members promptly identified process variations as one of the factors contributing to the lack of timeliness of referrals and follow-ups.

According to the flowchart, the intake nurse assessed patients prior to admission and completed service inquiries for those requiring therapy. These inquiries passed through the intake department, where an admission assistant filled out a therapy referral form and called therapists/agencies to assign patients as they were admitted. However, some patients are referred to Parker from its nursing facility or the community with a need for immediate treatment; in such cases, the intake nurse would make an immediate assessment so therapy could begin concurrently with admission. Service inquiries were delayed because nurses did not phone them in with other admission information, but waited until all admission paperwork was handed in to the intake department. This breakdown in the process could delay therapy referrals by several days. One of the team's immediate actions was to call for all intake nurses to use one standard procedure for therapy referrals, regardless of the patient's admission status. The therapy referral is given to the admission assistant as soon as the start of care date is known, whether or not accompanying paperwork has been completed.

Although this action helped the situation, it did not get to the root of the problem. The performance improvement team studied 23 late visits, 19 of which had causes for lateness documented in the clinical record. From this information and the process outlined in the flowchart, the team created a fishbone diagram to identify the root causes of late visits and follow-ups (Figure 6–2, page 114). The most consistent causes included the following:

- Late referrals were given to the admission assistant (31%);

- Language barriers prevented patients from understanding that visits were to be made, the purpose of the visit, and so on (26%);

- The therapist was late due to scheduling difficulties (21%);

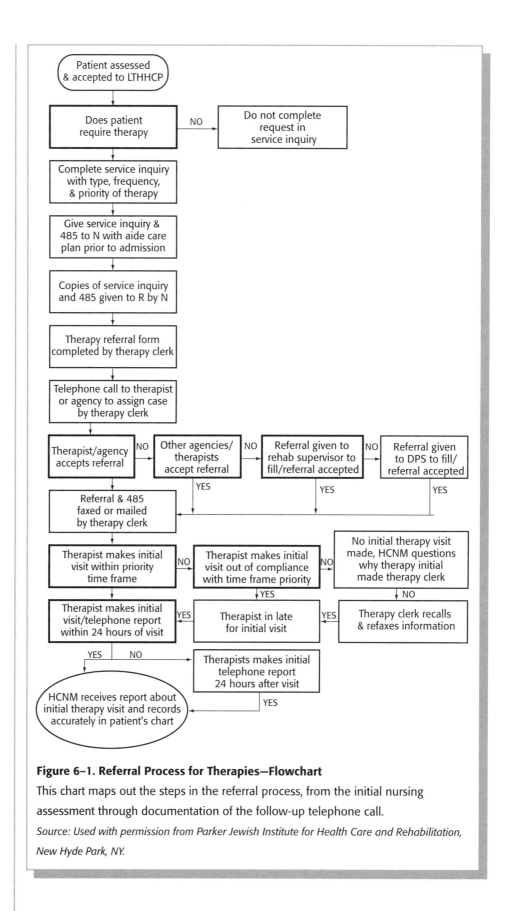

**Figure 6–1. Referral Process for Therapies—Flowchart**

This chart maps out the steps in the referral process, from the initial nursing assessment through documentation of the follow-up telephone call.

*Source: Used with permission from Parker Jewish Institute for Health Care and Rehabilitation, New Hyde Park, NY.*

- The patient or aide refused to admit the therapist (11%); and

- The therapist had difficulty contacting the patient (11%).

The problems were prioritized according to the percentages, and team members suggested and evaluated various improvement options for each:

- *Late referrals.* Although intake nurses had been informed about the one procedure to be used for all therapy referrals, this procedure was not always put into practice. To address this continuing problem, the team decided an in-service was required for staff involved in the admissions process to familiarize them with the new procedure and what it was meant to accomplish.

- *Language barriers.* A large percentage of Parker's patient population is Russian speaking and understands little or no English. The team identified several methods to address this problem, including the use of a special AT&T language line (which provides translation services for callers in almost any language), the hiring of bilingual therapists, and staff education regarding the need to have a translator available for all disciplines.

- *Poor scheduling.* Another in-service was deemed necessary for therapists to emphasize the importance of timely visits and follow-up calls.

- *Patient/aide refusal of visit.* The language barrier was often one element of refusal to admit a therapist to the home. Another was a lack of patient understanding as to the need for a specific type of therapy and what it would entail. The team ascertained that patient education was needed in this area for all disciplines.

- *Inability to contact patient.* Patient education was also needed to explain the importance of patients or aides being available to home care staff and of having an English-speaking friend or family member available during visits if the therapist was not bilingual.

"We tried to pinpoint and come up with solutions for each of the problems," says Ms Morahan. "Then we used the PDCA [Plan-Do-Check-Act] method to make improvements."

### Taking Action

Following the PDCA process, the team planned for each of the intended improvements. The intake supervisor drafted a written revision to the referral procedure based on the changes to which the team had already agreed. Parker recruited bilingual therapists by placing advertisements in professional publications. The rehabilitation supervisor designed in-services for in-house staff, as well as for therapists and vendor agencies.

Next was the step of implementing the improvements (doing). Parker hired a physical therapist who fluently spoke Russian. An in-service was held for nursing staff to teach them about the revised intake procedure and to emphasize the continued need for comprehensive patient education about services and treatment,

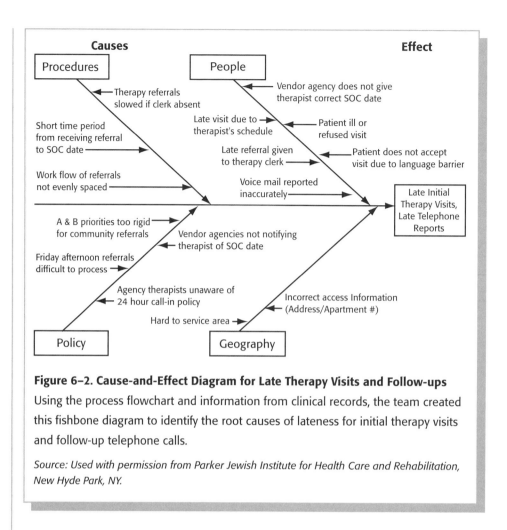

**Figure 6–2. Cause-and-Effect Diagram for Late Therapy Visits and Follow-ups**
Using the process flowchart and information from clinical records, the team created
this fishbone diagram to identify the root causes of lateness for initial therapy visits
and follow-up telephone calls.

*Source: Used with permission from Parker Jewish Institute for Health Care and Rehabilitation,
New Hyde Park, NY.*

thus allowing patients and their families to be active participants in the care plan.
In-services were also given to therapists and vendor agencies focusing on Parker's
policies and procedures for timely visits and telephone conferences, the availability of the language line, the use of telephone conference sheets to ensure complete
reports, and the procedure for documenting follow-up calls in progress notes.

*Checking Improvements and Holding the Gain*

To check the progress achieved by the actions taken, the rehabilitation supervisor
continued to use her clinical record reviews to collect data on the timeliness of initial therapy visits and follow-up telephone calls. Using fourth-quarter 1997 results
as a baseline, the team was able to see a 23% increase in the number of visits made
within the specified time frame and a 10% increase in the number of follow-up
calls made on time by the fourth quarter of 1998.

As the program went on, the rehabilitation supervisor forwarded results of clinical
record reviews to the home care administrator, and they were reported to the
home care program's overall quality improvement committee and to Parker's
main quality assurance and improvement committee every two months. The
information was also disseminated at nursing department meetings, to therapists
via memos and meetings, and on a facility bulletin board where results of various

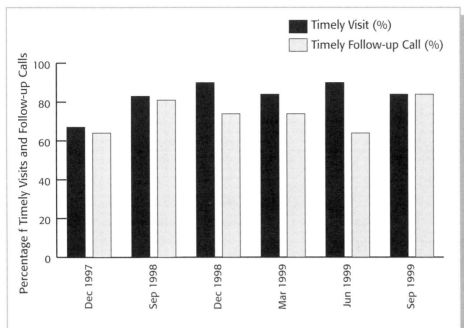

**Figure 6–3. Improvement in Timeliness of Initial Therapy Visits and Follow-up Telephone Conferences**

This bar chart illustrates the ongoing results from data collection regarding visits and follow-up calls made within the specified time frames. When a significant decline was noted, the performance improvement team went through the process again to determine root causes, find solutions, and implement solutions.

*Source: Used with permission from Parker Jewish Institute for Health Care and Rehabilitation, New Hyde Park, NY.*

improvement activities are posted regularly. The performance improvement team also gave a presentation at Parker's organizationwide annual quality assurance and improvement meeting in 1999. Quarterly results for the program are shown in Figure 6–3 (above).

Fluctuations in results sometimes prompted the performance improvement team to go back and reanalyze potential problems. For example, a dip in the number of follow-up calls being made on a timely basis prompted the team to review documentation for the root cause(s). It was found that one of the predominant reasons for lateness of follow-up calls was inconsistent reporting of calls received via voicemail afterhours on Friday and during the weekend. The progress notes often showed that the calls came in on Monday, thereby skewing the data and making it appear that calls and/or visits were late. Nurses received verbal reminders to report the actual dates the reports were received rather than the dates they were recorded.

### Lessons Learned and Looking Ahead

The Parker home care program continues to monitor the timeliness of initial therapy visits and follow-up conference calls between nurses and therapists and trend the data from record reviews. In addressing this problem, staff found that data collection did not have to be a cumbersome extra step, nor did data analysis need to include complex statistical formulas to be effective. Data collection was part of an ongoing record review, and compilation was a matter of comparing the total number of records to the number of records in which visits and phone calls were documented appropriately.

Still, not every improvement project is the same—those that address a larger patient population or involve more paperwork may call for more sophisticated tools and methods. For example, Parker's home care program has begun looking at inconsistencies between care plans and aide duty sheets. With approximately 1,000 duty sheets coming in to the main office each week, it would be impossible to review all of them for identified performance measures on a regular basis. "We have a research center at Parker," explains Ms Morahan. "And we may involve them from the beginning on the next project just to make sure we're doing things right—using samples of a correct number of records and that sort of thing. But we want to keep the process manageable." That's sound advice for any performance improvement project.

# Case Study #2: Behavioral Health
# Hazelden Center City Recovery Services

The Hazelden Foundation's alcohol and drug treatment facility in Center City, Minnesota, provides outpatient recovery services, residential family care, primary residential treatment (approximately 180 beds), and continuing and extended care. In July 1998, the nursing department of the Health Services Unit of Recovery Services at Hazelden Center City and Fairview Lakes Regional Healthcare (which provides contracted pharmaceutical services to Center City) began a collaborative effort to improve the processes for identifying, reporting, and reducing the number of adverse drug events (ADEs) at the behavioral health facility. This was prompted, in part, by the rising level of clinical acuity in the patient population and a corresponding rise in medication doses being dispensed. ADEs (or medication errors) had also come to the fore in the literature as one of the health care industry's most common and costly problems.

## Getting Started

A performance improvement team was formed to address the matter of ADEs. It comprised the administrative assistant for nursing (who served as the team leader), the nurse manager of health services, four nursing supervisors, various members of the nursing staff, the quality coordinator, and the contracted pharmacist and several pharmacy staff members from Fairview. As the team began to look at the problem and develop goals for the project, two initial barriers were identified.

First, the ultimate goal of decreasing the number of ADEs was clear, but the way to achieve it was not. Although Center City routinely monitored "medication errors," like many health care organizations, it traditionally had not categorized the why and how of what had occurred (for example, a medication being omitted versus an incorrect dose being given). The facility also had no standardized method of tracking ADEs. "There was inconsistent data collection prior to this project," explains Jon Zeipen, MSW, coordinator of quality measurement at Center City. "There was a lot of anecdotal information. We only had about 20 reports of medication errors per quarter, and those weren't consistent." Thus, there was little quantitative data to use as a baseline for improvement efforts.

Second, the pervading perception among many health care professionals across the continuum is that ADEs are an individual performance issue rather than an organizationwide process issue. The level of staff compliance with reporting and documenting ADEs was low, reflecting this mind-set. Without staff cooperation, the data collected for the project would necessarily be incomplete and inaccurate.

It was obvious that changing staff members' existing attitude would be as necessary and basic to the success of improvement activities as developing the methodology for data collection and analysis. The ADE team decided on the following goals for the project:

- Create a shift in the existing culture from one of judgment/blame to one of learning regarding the way ADEs are perceived and reported; and

- Develop a new systematic method of tracking and reporting ADEs.

*Setting the Wheels in Motion*

The team members first worked together to create a Medication Occurrence Reporting Form to be used for data collection at all sites where medications were dispensed (in addition to its main medical unit, Center City has several satellite nursing stations within the facility where patients can receive medications). The form focused on the five areas the ADE team had chosen as the most important for this phase of the project:

- The number of ADEs per month;

- The number of potential ADEs per month;

- The apparent causes of ADEs (transcription errors, dispensing delays, and so forth);

- The types of ADEs (wrong dose, wrong medication, and so forth); and

- The percentage of ADEs relative to the total number of doses administered per quarter.

In addition to this information, the form also asked whether the medication error actually reached the patient (Was it caught before administration?) and the degree of any resulting injury. The team used the literature and similar forms from Fairview Lakes Regional Healthcare as starting points for this tool.

To prepare staff for participation in the measurement process, the nurse manager of health services and the contracted pharmacist conducted in-services to familiarize nurses with the form and to explain the purpose of its use. The instructors emphasized the need for collecting data in order to identify trends as the first step to improving processes, which would ultimately improve patient care. They also highlighted the organization's desire to learn about and fix or improve its processes instead of judging whether staff members were doing something wrong. "We needed to take the fear out of the process to get people to report events," says Chris Lind, RN, nurse manager of health services at Center City. "Staff buy-in was the most important thing."

Forms were collected on a weekly basis and given to the quality measurement department, where a staff member categorized them as ADEs, potential ADEs, or neither. The information was keyed into a database and printed out in spreadsheet form. Department staff then created a number of charts to display the data for analysis by the ADE team. These included bar charts showing the number of ADEs and potential ADEs per month, Pareto charts showing the "vital few" apparent causes and types of ADEs each month, and a bar chart illustrating ADEs versus potential ADEs on a quarterly basis. Cumulative percentage charts could be produced after several quarters to trend the results (Figure 6-4, page 119).

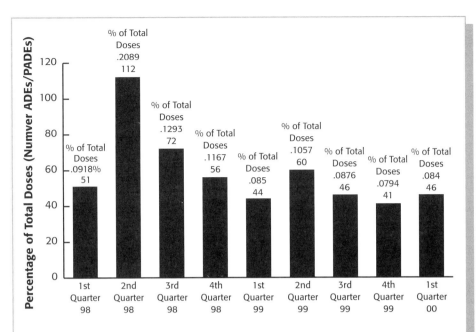

**Figure 6–4. Percentage of Actual Adverse Drug Events (ADEs) and Potential Adverse Drug Events (PADEs) per Number of Doses Given**

This bar chart shows the trend in ADEs reported over a two-year period. The high peaks in 1998 correspond with the beginning of Center City's performance improvement project and the beginning of staff education, when the importance of reporting incidents was first emphasized. The lower numbers for late 1999 and early 2000 may be attributed to fewer incidents occurring and/or to less stringent reporting; additional information is needed to make this determination.

*Source: Used with permission from Hazelden Foundation, Center City, MN.*

*Taking Action*

The performance improvement team met quarterly to examine the data, target specific areas of concern, and prioritize which causes and types of ADEs to watch most carefully. As time went on and team members were able to see specific trends in causes and types of actual and potential ADEs (Figure 6–5, page 120), they began to plan improvement activities based on these trends. They developed a flowchart of the medication administration process to determine where break-downs were most likely to occur (Figure 6–6, page 121). Using both the flowchart and the information from control charts, they were able to find ways of streamlining the process to reduce ADEs.

Dispensing errors were, and continue to be, the most frequent causes of ADEs (Figure 6–7, page 122). "We looked at this category in more detail and identified two basic areas that caused problems," says Mark Nelson, pharmacy manager at Fairview Lakes Regional Healthcare. "One was tapers (patients whose doses increase or decrease over time), and the other was wrong medication, or pharmacy filling orders incorrectly." The team found that the tapers problem was mainly one of scheduling—nursing and pharmacy staffs needed to agree on the same schedules for the withdrawal or augmentation of doses. Team members worked together to establish consistent schedules, and nurses and pharmacists were made aware of them. The pharmacy staff at Fairview addressed the problem of wrong medications being dispensed, revising its internal procedures for profiling.

### Monitoring Results and Looking Ahead

Results from improvement efforts were (and are) shared at nursing staff meetings at Center City and pharmacy staff meetings at Fairview. The quality measurement department added a new control chart to its Quality Report, a monthly report on all of the center's performance improvement projects that is sent to select recovery services staff (primarily administrators, supervisors, and managers) and to organizational administrators of Hazelden's national recovery services. The chart tracks the number of medication occurrence reports completed quarterly per the total number of medication doses; the team set the benchmark at 50 (Figure 6–8, page 123).

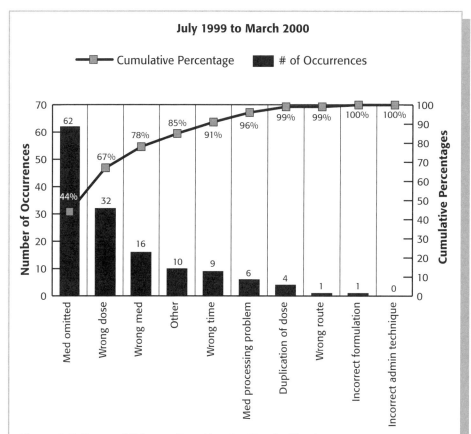

**Figure 6–5. Types of Adverse Drug Events—Pareto Chart**

This Pareto chart is an example of how the most common types of ADEs are trended over time. This information is used in conjunction with similar charts for causes of ADEs to identify parts of the process that need revision. Because the "other" category represented such a large percentage, the Hazelden team has since broken out another measure—"administration exceeds order"—for examination.

*Source: Used with permission from Hazelden Foundation, Center City, MN.*

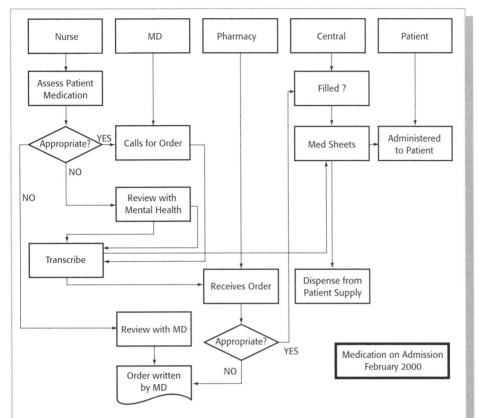

**Figure 6–6. The Medication Administration Process—Flowchart**
The adverse drug events team created a flowchart to identify problem spots within the administration process. The flowchart has been streamlined as effective resolutions to problems have been found.

*Source: Used with permission from Hazelden Foundation, Center City, MN.*

The number of ADEs reported is higher than it was at the start of the project, evidence that the desired change in corporate culture is taking place. Although the highest numbers were predictably seen immediately after staff education regarding data collection first began, results have evened off at or near the proposed benchmark. The lower numbers may be attributed to the effectiveness of improvement efforts rather than a decrease in reporting. "You can see by that chart that we've come a long way from where we started," states Mr Zeipen, "but it's a work in progress. We're going to keep looking at the data and see if we can continue to pinpoint the areas where problems may be occurring."

Ms Lind agrees that the project will remain ongoing. "I originally looked at this as a five-year project," she says. "The kind of cultural shift we wanted necessitated a slow process." Many organizations miss or belittle the importance of staff buy-in to the improvement process. However, since staff members are usually the people who perform at least preliminary tasks in ongoing data collection, their lack of support and compliance can jeopardize the accuracy and value of the data—and by extension, all activities based on those data.

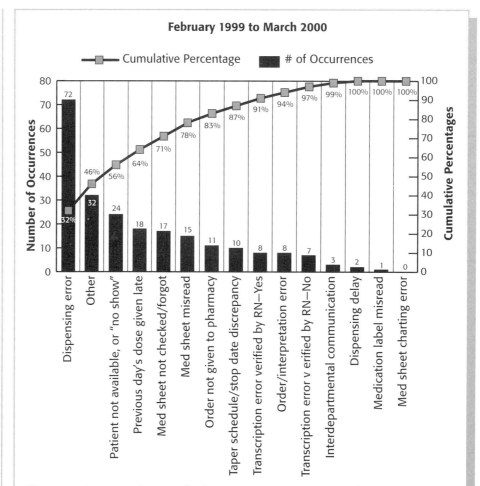

**Figure 6-7. Apparent Causes of Adverse Drug Events—Pareto Chart**

This sample Pareto chart shows which of the common causes of adverse drug events are most prevalent over one year. Used in conjunction with the process flowchart, this type of information helps the performance improvement team zero in on parts of the process that need to be improved. Because the "other" category represented such a large percentage, the Hazelden team has since broken out two more measures—"profiled as filled, not found" and "pharmacy transcription error"—for examination.

*Source: Used with permission from Hazelden Foundation, Center City, MN.*

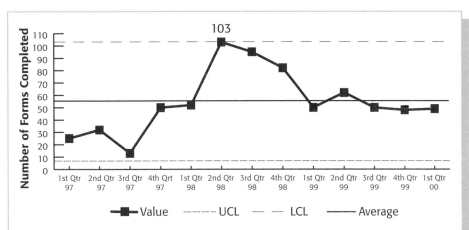

**Figure 6–8. Number of Medication Occurrence Report Forms Completed per Number of Medication Doses—Benchmark (50) Control Chart**

This control chart accompanies the monthly organizationwide quality report to keep administrators and supervisors apprised of the adverse drug events project's progress. The ratio measure is shown for each quarter, and the number of medication doses remains fairly constant, at about 52,000.

*Source: Used with permission from Hazelden Foundation, Center City, MN.*

## Case Study #3: Hospital
## South County Hospital

A 100-bed facility in Wakefield, Rhode Island, South County Hospital offers patients a full range of services (excepting neurologic or cardiac surgery). Because performance improvement is an integral part of South County's strategic plan, the organization was enthusiastic about participating in the early stages of the Joint Commission's ORYX Initiative. In 1997 the hospital's performance improvement committee looked at the suggested indicators for the initiative and chose to address those that fit their criteria for indicator selection (high risk, high volume, problem prone). These indicators—which were chosen with input from the medical staff—included one perioperative measure, one obstetric measure, two cardiovascular measures, two oncology measures, one trauma measure, two medication use measures, and one infection control measure; they were incorporated into South County's existing performance improvement program, and data collection began in July 1998.

### Close-up on Creatinine

One of the medication use measures the hospital chose to study was the number of patients 65 or older in whom creatinine clearance was estimated or measured. "We knew this was an area where there was a good opportunity for improvement," remembers Elaine Vieira, RN, CCRN, BS, manager for performance improvement and corporate compliance. "About 85% to 90% of our patient population is over the age of 65, so we felt we could make drastic improvements for a large number of people."

The multidisciplinary team charged with examining this measure included representatives from pharmacy, nursing, laboratory, information services, and performance improvement and corporate compliance. Team members decided that their overall goal was to increase the number of patients over age 65 who would have an estimated or actual measure of creatinine clearance early in their hospital stay. Pharmacy personnel were assigned the responsibility of estimating the creatinine clearance levels for the target population based on each patient's age, sex, weight, and serum creatinine number. Although the first two elements were readily available from the patient's chart, the other two were not. The team flowcharted the process and found that changes needed to be made (Figure 6–9, page 125).

To correct this problem, information services staff looked at existing computer capabilities for the collection of the necessary patient data, as well as what would be possible with anticipated systems in both the laboratory and pharmacy. Nursing staff record patient weight on the admission interview form, which is not easily accessible to the pharmacy. However, the pharmacy does receive copies of physicians' order sheets for all patients. It was decided that nurses would transfer weight data from admission interview forms to the order sheets, which are faxed to the pharmacy on a daily basis. To make the serum creatinine number available

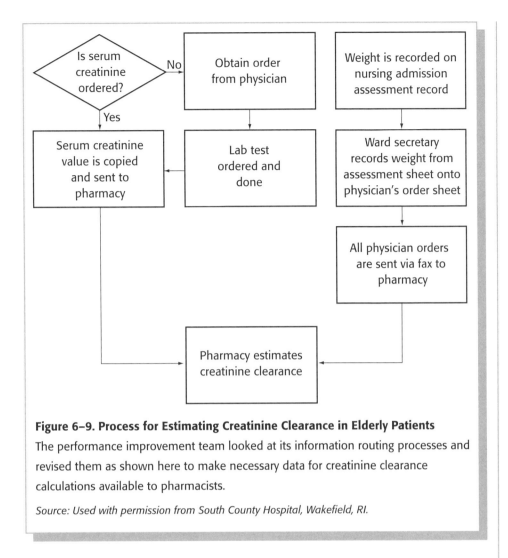

**Figure 6–9. Process for Estimating Creatinine Clearance in Elderly Patients**

The performance improvement team looked at its information routing processes and revised them as shown here to make necessary data for creatinine clearance calculations available to pharmacists.

*Source: Used with permission from South County Hospital, Wakefield, RI.*

to pharmacists, laboratory staff gather the results of tests for serum creatinine levels and fax them to the pharmacy daily.

*Finding the Facts*

Given the high percentage of elderly patients at South County, collecting necessary data for the project might have seemed like a daunting task. However, the hospital was able to integrate initial data collection for this and other performance improvement projects through ORYX. A staff person in the performance improvement office enters all data from patient medical records, and these data are sent to the ORYX system. The system generates reports on patients, including names and medical record numbers, relating to each of the specified indicators, and forwards them to the hospital. South County staff then pulls the appropriate medical records (an average of 250 per month) using a software program that interfaces with the ORYX software. Each medical record is reviewed for information on all appropriate indicators.

For the creatinine clearance project, the pharmacy submits a monthly or quarterly list of all patients for whom it has performed an estimated creatinine clearance.

The laboratory provides a list of the actual measurements that were done during the same time period. These data are entered into the computer and given to the ORYX system. Original baseline data collected from July 1998 to March 1999 showed that average compliance with estimated creatinine clearance calculations was 6% (Figure 6–10, page 127).

System reports show the "what" (how many patients actually had an estimated or actual creatinine clearance calculation performed), but they do not address the "why" (reasons calculations were not made), so when the creatinine clearance team implemented plans for an improved process in November 1999, it also asked information services to create a software program with which it could make calculations in-house. The resulting spreadsheet lets the team drill down ORYX results to find root causes for noncompliance. It includes each of the necessary elements for calculations (age, sex, weight, serum creatinine level) and is used by pharmacy staff, who monitor which patients have had actual or estimated creatinine clearance calculations. If a calculation was not performed for a specific patient, the pharmacist indicates whether problematic data elements (weight and/or serum creatinine level) were not provided, or whether there was a pharmacy-related process problem that prevented calculation. For example, the following data were collected for December 1999:

| | |
|---|---|
| Total patients with estimated creatinine clearance | 60 |
| Total patients 65 and older | 221 |
| Compliance rate | 27% |
| Weight not documented | 50% |
| Serum creatinine value not available | 8% |
| Weight and serum creatinine not documented | 14% |

Ms Vieira analyzes such data to pinpoint at what stage of the process most problems occur. "Patient weight has consistently been the most frequently missed element," she notes. "Although it appears in every medical record, it is not routinely made available to pharmacists." All of these results were reported back to the hospitalwide performance improvement committee in January 2000.

### Revising Data Capture Processes

After examining the quantifiable information about what was hindering compliance with the creatinine clearance indicator, the performance improvement committee appointed the nurse managers to look at ways to improve the transmission of weight data to the pharmacy. By performing a root cause analysis, the managers found that staff were not consistently writing the patient's weight in both the admission interview record and the physician's order sheet. To address this dilemma, nurses began to use a logbook in which each new admission was listed. At the end of each shift, the ward secretary checked each new admission record to

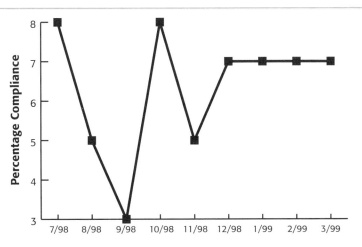

| Month | Number of Medical Records | % Compliance with Estimated Creatinine Clearance |
|---|---|---|
| July 1998 | 312 | 8% |
| August 1998 | 349 | 5% |
| September 1998 | 229 | 3% |
| October 1998 | 237 | 8% |
| November 1998 | 220 | 5% |
| December 1998 | 263 | 7% |
| January 1999 | 220 | 7% |
| February 1999 | 228 | 7% |
| March 1999 | 263 | 7% |
| Totals | 2,321 | 6% overall compliance |

Drill down of the causative factors continues to reveal that patient weight is the missing data element. Will report to director of acute services and the performance improvement committee for further follow-up.

**Figure 6–10. Baseline Data for Indicator Compliance**

This run chart shows the initial ORYX results for the number of patients aged 65 or older with estimated or actual creatinine clearance calculations performed. Percentage of compliance ranged from 8% to 3%, with an overall average of 6%. The number of applicable medical records reviewed each month ranged from 349 to 220, with an average of 258.

*Source: Used with permission from South County Hospital, Wakefield, RI.*

be sure that weight was recorded on the physician's order sheet and sent to the pharmacy.

## Charting Progress and Future Needs

Results from follow-up data collection reflected a notable increase in estimates of creatinine clearance compared to baseline results (Figure 6–11, page 128). After the first jump, though, the rate has remained relatively the same, with an average of about 21%. This is a common occurrence in many performance improvement projects, and ongoing monitoring is especially important as more process changes are made to show which changes take the compliance rate above the plateau.

Although compliance has gone up, South County staff want it to improve further. They feel this indicator is especially meaningful because of the large number of elderly patients they serve—patients who have the most comorbidities and are most likely to receive multiple medications. Estimated creatinine clearance provides important information for pharmacists to use in assessing the medication regimens of these patients. The logbook has helped a little, but sending weight information to the pharmacy is still a problem. According to Ms Vieria, "We're going to go back to the drawing board to try to figure out a better way of doing

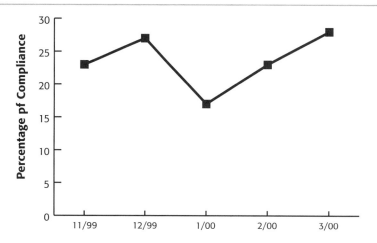

| Month | Number of Medical Records | % Compliance with estimated Creatinine Clearance |
|---|---|---|
| November 1999 | 144 | 24% |
| December 1999 | 221 | 27% |
| January 2000 | 258 | 19% |
| February 2000 | 257 | 25% |
| March 2000 | 253 | 30% |
| April 2000 | 171 | 40% |
| May 2000 | 157 | 33% |
| June 2000 | 253 | 31% |

Drill down of the causative factors continues to reveal that patient weight is the missing data element. Report will be submitted to the performance improvement committee for further follow-up.

**Figure 6–11. Follow-up Data for Indicator Compliance**
More recent data collection showed significant improvement in compliance following initial process changes in November 1999. After that, improvement was slower, averaging 21% for five months.

*Source: Used with permission from South County Hospital, Wakefield, RI.*

this. We really want to pursue software options and see if there is anything we can build into our new systems to make this work more smoothly. Fortunately, we're a small hospital, which makes communication easier." And communication is a key factor in the success of any performance improvement project.

## Case Study #4: Health System
## North Shore–Long Island Jewish Health System

North Shore–Long Island Jewish Health System (NS-LIJHS) in New York comprises both owned and sponsored hospitals; nursing homes; ambulatory facilities; rehabilitation, home care, hospice, and behavioral health programs; practitioner sites; and a managed care plan. Approximately 172,000 inpatients are served throughout the system each year. Each organization within the system as a whole has a multidisciplinary performance improvement coordinating group (PICG) that identifies and prioritizes improvement projects, recommends actions to be taken, and reports results of improvement activities. It was at the suggestion of the systemwide PICG and other network advisory committees that the system pressure injury* committee was formed in August 1996.

The suggestion was partially based on the Agency for Health Care Policy and Research's (AHCPR's) 1992 publication of guidelines to predict, prevent, and treat pressure ulcers. It was also rooted in the results from a study conducted by the Island Peer Review Organization (IPRO) in 1994. Six hospitals and one long term care organization from the network participated in this study, which consisted of retrospective chart review for a large sample of cerebrovascular accident patients and identified pressure injuries as a statewide priority. The findings from the study were shared with NS-LIJHS's quality management department and all participating organizations. The network determined that opportunities for improvement existed in the areas of patient assessment and reassessment, risk assessment, and prevention and interventions.

*Setting the Stage*

The team that was put together to address pressure injuries across the system included clinical experts from hospitals, long term care organizations, and home care agencies. Members included nurses, physicians, enterostomal therapists, physical therapists, quality management coordinators, educators, nutritionists, and pharmacists, all of whom were chosen based on their expertise in wound care management. Staff from the systemwide quality management department and materials support services were included to help coordinate activities among facilities. The team met monthly for the two years following its inception and continues to meet quarterly. Committee members are responsible for reporting recommendations and project status to their respective facilities.

The team was charged with developing guidelines for predicting, preventing, and treating pressure injuries based on AHCPR recommendations. Its specific aims were to

---

*In its efforts to standardize definitions across the network, the committee agreed to use the term* injury *instead of* ulcer *to correspond with current staging guidelines that include redness in the characteristics for this condition.*

- standardize risk assessment methodologies and specific time frames for patient assessment (on admission) and reassessment (within seven days);

- establish a uniform skin care product line across the system and control costs through resource utilization monitoring and price negotiations with a limited number of vendors; and

- develop standardized measurements and reporting formats to be used by all network facilities.

As with other systemwide performance improvement projects, the committee used Shewhart's Plan-Do-Check-Act (PDCA) cycle in conjunction with the Joint Commission's ten-step methodology.

Network and organization leaders participated in prioritizing, planning, and implementing the pressure injury initiative. "I don't think the importance of leadership's contribution can be overemphasized," states Yosef Dlugacz, PhD, the system's senior vice president for quality management. "They legitimized the project by supporting changes in resource allocation and effective communication between organizations." In addition to allocating necessary financial resources, leaders ensured that personnel were available to conduct orientation and in-services, to maintain quality control programs and ongoing performance measurement, and to take action to improve performance per recommendations. This supportive attitude facilitated the coordination of activities among and within individual organizations and the adoption of new processes and guidelines.

### Taking Action

The pressure injury committee first reviewed the literature and all existing skin care protocols (a wide variety of risk assessment tools were used throughout the network) to determine best practices. In October 1996, the Braden scale—comprising sensory perception, skin moisture, activity, mobility, nutritional intake, and friction and shear—was adopted as the systemwide risk assessment tool for predicting pressure injuries based on committee recommendations and approval by clinical staff and leadership. This scale was chosen because of its good interrater reliability rate and ease of use. Staff were educated in its use via a systemwide teleconference in December 1996.

To address the problem of resource utilization, pressure injury team members worked with materials support services staff to investigate the use of skin care products and specialty beds. They found that among system organizations, more than 100 skin care products and two specialty bed companies were used. By mid-1997, the committee had pared down the number considerably. "We looked at the products and the literature, and then streamlined the formulary from 140 products to 24," says Lori Stier, RN, EdD, administrative director for quality management. "This represents a big financial savings because the system can buy in bulk for all its components, and it offers consistency of high-quality skin care across settings." By the end of the year, NS-LIJHS had also interviewed three specialty bed companies and selected one to serve its entire system.

*Following the Numbers*

The performance measures/indicators used in the pressure injury project are listed in Table 6–1 (below). In early 1998, NS-LIJHS developed a partnership with Hill-Rom (the system's specialty bed vendor) to perform baseline prevalence studies for the project before introducing new system guidelines for pressure injuries, which had been developed by the committee and approved by clinical staff from all acute care organizations. Trained personnel from the company went to six system acute care facilities and worked with nurses on the units to collect data pertaining to the established measures through chart reviews and bedside inspections with handheld computers. The software program used was designed specifically for data collection related to pressure injuries. The sample comprised all patients except for those on obstetrics and postpartum units, newborn nurseries, and psychiatric units, which were judged to be low-risk populations. Hill-Rom aggregated the data—which were not randomized, stratified, or risk adjusted—and created prevalence summaries (spreadsheets). System data were compared to national results, and the overall prevalence rate (14.2%) was found to be lower than the national average (17.1%). The network's prevalence of nosocomial pressure injuries (7.6%) also came out below the national percentage (10.2%). Findings were presented to the system's nurse executives and PICGs.

Another systemwide teleconference was held in March 1998 to inform staff about the new system guidelines for predicting, preventing, and treating pressure injuries. The conference was developed and presented by clinicians from acute care, long term care, and home care. Follow-up prevalence studies were conducted

---

**Table 6–1. Pressure Injury Performance Measures**

- Pressure injury prevalence rate (system and national)
- Nosocomial pressure injury prevalence rate (system and national)
- Braden score
- High-risk patients (%)
- Moderate-risk patients (%)
- Low-risk patients (%)
- No-risk patients (%)
- Percentage of pressure injuries by stage (I–IV)
- Location of pressure injuries (sacral, buttocks, heels)
- Source of injury
  - Admitted from home with injury (%)
  - Admitted from nursing home with injury (%)
  - Admitted from acute care facility with injury (%)
- Pressure injury documentation (%)
- Skin assessment completed within 24 hours (%)
- Nutritional consult performed (%)
- Patients receiving topical treatments for injuries (%)
- Patients on recommended sleep surfaces (%)

---

in early 1999 to determine the effectiveness of the new guidelines. System averages were again lower than national rates. Results from the surveys were disseminated to each participating organization's PICG and to network leadership in a report from the quality management department that combined spreadsheets and graphics.

## Monitoring Outcomes

The system has established an internal database that uses comparative data from its various organizations for benchmarking (Figure 6–12, below, and Figure 6–13, page 134). In addition to the results from prevalence studies, comparisons are also drawn against the findings from the national Multi-site Pressure Ulcer Prevalence Study (1995–1997), which measured the prevalence of nosocomial pressure ulcers in 922 hospitals.

Although no significant change was seen in overall prevalence and nosocomial injury rates (14.5% and 7.6%, respectively, for 1999), the number of Stage III and Stage IV pressure injuries was reduced in 1999; Figure 6–14 (page 135) shows a

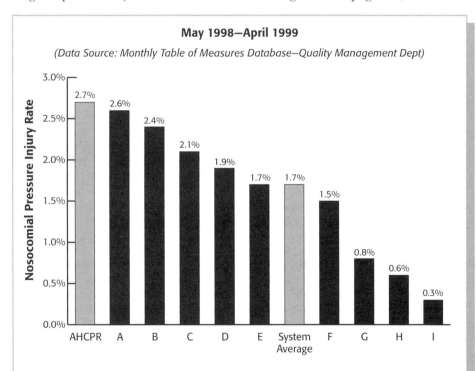

**Figure 6–12. Nosocomial Pressure Injury Rate at North Shore–Long Island Jewish Health System**

This bar chart represents a descriptive analysis of nosocomial pressure injury rates by hospital. Data were not risk adjusted; however, a profile of these patients reveals similar characteristics with respect to age (geriatric), diagnosis, and length of stay. Rates for individual organizations are plotted next to the national average. A system average is also shown.

*Source: Used with permission of Quality Management Department, North Shore–Long Island Jewish Health System, Great Neck, NY.*

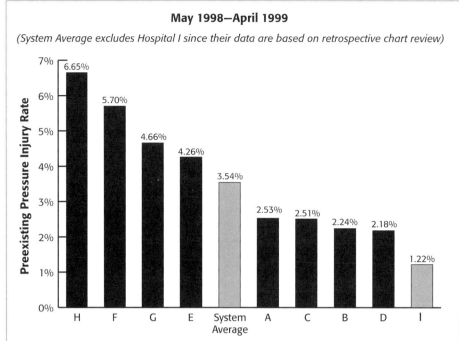

**May 1998–April 1999**

*(System Average excludes Hospital I since their data are based on retrospective chart review)*

**Figure 6–13. Rate of Admissions with Preexisting Pressure Injuries at North Shore–Long Island Jewish Health System**

This chart illustrates the rates of preexisting (community-acquired) pressure injuries by hospital. Individual organizations are ranked against each other and the system average.

*Source: Used with permission of Quality Management Department, North Shore–Long Island Jewish Health System, Great Neck, NY.*

downward trend in length of stay. The system is still examining individual performance measures to determine where improvements have been most effective, but the new guidelines and resource management (skin care products and specialty beds) instituted during 1998 and 1999 have had a definite effect on programs within organizations. "Patient assessment was the biggest problem," says Ms Stier. "So medical record forms were changed to embed the Braden scale in the initial nursing assessment." Several system hospitals have begun to assess high-risk patients on a daily basis rather than every seven days as required, and some that did not have formal skin care programs before 1998 now have dedicated nurses in charge of this area. The system guidelines, originally developed for acute care, were modified for long term care and home care facilities, which use them as standards of care. The guidelines also provide a basis for understanding network hospitals' and nursing homes' skin care regimens and injury treatments so continuity of care is maintained.

In addition to patient-centered outcomes, the system has evaluated the financial outcomes of using common skin care products and one specialty bed vendor for all facilities. The total cost savings realized from using a single bed vendor was

$186,365 (24.7%) between 1997 and 1999. This was in addition to the savings experienced by individual organizations through purchasing skin care products in bulk quantities.

Looking ahead, North Shore–Long Island Jewish Health System will continue to monitor all performance measures, including readmissions of patients with pressure injuries. The necessarily broad scope of the pressure injury initiative presents an ongoing challenge. "We will continue to improve in surveillance and communication," says Dr Dlugacz. Continuing education efforts are planned to ensure that guidelines are being followed consistently across the continuum. The system also intends to examine the role of targeted nutrition in enhancing wound healing, especially in the elderly, across settings. Results so far indicate that improvements in patient outcomes can be attained in conjunction with improvements in financial outcomes.

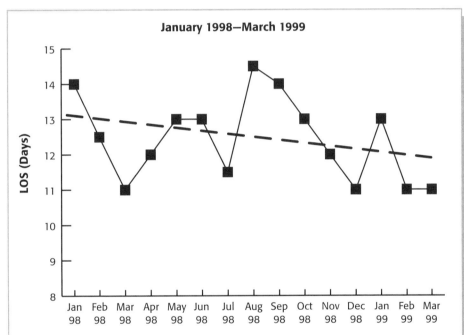

**Figure 6–14. Median Length of Stay for Patients with Pressure Injuries at North Shore–Long Island Jewish Health System**

This regression trend line shows a downward trend in length of stay since (LOS) the systemwide guidelines for pressure injuries were first implemented.

*Source: Used with permission of Quality Management Department, North Shore–Long Island Jewish Health System, Great Neck, NY.*

# Appendix A: Case Study Exercise

Christine McGreevey, RN, MS
Associate Project Director
Division of Research
Joint Commission on Accreditation of Healthcare Organizations
Oakbrook Terrace, Illinois

This long term care case study is presented as a self-study exercise. Most people find it easier to absorb concepts by applying them to real-life examples. Thus, readers are encouraged to use the information presented in this case study to review the data management principles explained in the earlier chapters. This example is based on the 1998 Codman Award for Long Term Care—Susquehanna Lutheran Village in Millersburg, Pennsylvania—for its restraint reduction initiative.*

## How to Use This Exercise

A brief introduction is given first, providing background on the organization (size, population, and so forth) that will be taken into account during the exercise. The steps for managing data as part of the restraint reduction program are presented as individual modules:

1. Study the information given in each module, and then read the review material at the end of the module.

2. Cover the answers to the right of the question with a strip of paper, and try to fill in the correct term for each blank space that has been left.

3. Check your answer against the answer given to the right. If yours is very different from the answer provided, return to the module and study the text again. Notes are provided throughout to give further explanation.

4. Once you understand the concept that is illustrated and have provided the correct answer, move on to the next module. Do not move ahead until you have mastered each concept in order.

## Background

Susquehanna Lutheran Village (SLV) is a 203-bed long term care facility licensed for skilled and intermediate care. It was affiliated with Tressler Lutheran Services (now Diakon Lutheran Social Ministries), and its performance improvement initiative to reduce the use of restraints began in 1995.

Throughout the process, the data the facility collected led to a focus on

---

*The data presented in this case study are not the exact data from Susquehanna Lutheran Village, but they are similar in content. The outcomes presented are the same as those shared by the Susquehanna staff at the Codman awards presentation on November 11, 1998.*

restraint-free care, not just reduction. Examples of restraints include bedside rails, chest poseys, soft wrist restraints, gerichairs with tables latched in place, and other methods used to restrict a resident's freedom of movement. The average age of SLV's resident population is 83 years; 80% of the population is female; and the average dementia population is 52%. During the course of this initiative, the resident population had an acuity index range of 0.39 to 3.93, and the index average remained between 0.99 and 1.06 during the entire process. No additional staff were required.

Initial efforts focused on decreasing the use of restraints within the facility. New admissions were not restrained, and restraints on residents arriving directly from the hospital were immediately discarded. The resident and his or her family were informed of this policy during the hospital intake interview. Bed and chair alarms were purchased, along with specially designed bed mattresses (whose outside edges were raised 1 to 2 inches) and protective floor mats. Current residents had restraints removed gradually over the first year of the program, less problematic residents first. After 18 months, the last 5% of residents (more problematic group) were targeted for methods to reduce restraints and keep the residents as safe as possible. Staff teams then brainstormed creative ways, unique to each resident, to ensure safety while leaving the residents unrestrained.

Based on a literature review, staff were aware that an increase in falls could be anticipated once restraint use was decreased, so they began to monitor falls and conduct a detailed analysis. They developed a Fall Analysis Form to aid in early identification of the causes of falls, including activity prior to the fall, time of day, location, hallway in which the resident resided, injuries and types, resident activity level, number of disoriented resident falls, number of residents using psychotropics, and monitors in use with falls (chair alarms and bed alarms were used for some residents).

At the same time, the director of social services and the continuous quality improvement coordinator took an active interest in promoting the Eden Alternative to administration and staff at SLV. The Eden Alternative seeks to eliminate the three plagues of long term care institutions: loneliness, helplessness, and boredom. It is based on the belief that nursing homes should become habitats for human beings rather than institutions for the frail and elderly. The companionship of animals, the opportunity to care for other living things, and the variety and spontaneity that mark an enlivened environment can succeed where pills and therapies fail.[1]

## Module 1: Basic Principles

Staff performed a thorough literature review to learn more about restraint use and to determine what other facilities had found successful in physical restraint reduction efforts. They learned from previous research ("Physical Restraints: A Dilemma in Long Term Care" by Gladys Thankachan) of the differences between nine long term care facilities in the Pennsylvania area (three had nonrestraining policies, and six allowed the use of physical restraints). Thankachan's four-month study, which was based on 641 incident reports, found that fewer falls with serious injuries occurred in the nonrestraining facilities (Figure A–1, below).

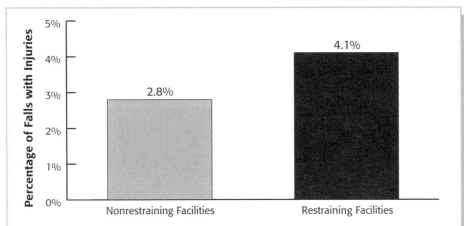

**Figure A–1. Percentage of Falls with Injuries, According to Type of Facility**
This simple bar chart shows the percentage of resident falls resulting in injuries as two differently shaded vertical bars along the x-axis. The y-axis is numbered 0% through 5% and shows the percentage of falls with injuries.

*Review*

Nursing home staff have traditionally believed that restraining residents was necessary to prevent the residents from harming themselves. However, through _____ _____, staff learned that inactivity (a result of restraint use) decreases muscle mass and bone density. So, inactive residents who fall are more likely to incur an injury, such as a hip fracture.

**literature review** *or* **investigational research**

*Note:* Restraint use also takes away a person's dignity and rights.

The bottom legend of the chart in Figure A–1 informs the user about the information plotted on the _____ of the chart, namely the restraining and nonrestraining facilities. The left side of the chart, or the _____, shows the measurement rate or percentage of falls resulting in injuries to residents.

**x-axis**

**y-axis**

## Module 2: Finding Baselines for Selected Performance Measures

In 1995, at the start of the restraint reduction initiative, SLV used the following performance measures:

*Rate of restraint use* (data collected monthly):

*Numerator:*   Those residents who experienced one or more episodes in which they were physically restrained (with any type of physical or mechanical device used to limit movement, physical activity, or normal access in order to protect the resident)

*Denominator:*   All residents

*Rate of falls* (data collected monthly):

*Numerator:*   Those residents who experienced one or more falls (where the resident dropped from a higher to a lower level or position with or without a resulting injury)

*Denominator:*   All residents

*Rate of falls with injury* (data collected monthly):

*Numerator:*   All resident falls that resulted in injuries (requiring physician intervention/treatment and resulting in a temporary or permanent change in the resident's activities of daily living)

*Denominator:*   All resident falls

The facility's *baseline statistics* for these measures were as follows:

| Measure Name | Proportion (Rate) | Percentage |
|---|---|---|
| Rate of restraint use | 0.64 | 64% |
| Rate of falls | 0.11 | 11% |
| Rate of falls with injuries | 0.0325 | 3.25% |

The alternative restraint team was formed to work on different aspects of the initiative. Measurement data were used to monitor and validate whether implemented changes were having the desired effects. The team's initial plan included the following:

- Proactively informing neighborhood hospitals about SLV's restraint-free goal and that new residents transferred from a hospital would receive a preadmission (intake) assessment at the hospital by a trained nursing home staff member to assess the resident's physical/mental status and needs. Future residents and their families were told that upon admission to the nursing home no restraints would be used, and they were given examples of alternatives that would be used to keep the resident safe.

- Calculating the monthly rates of restraints in use by device type for monthly continuous quality improvement meetings.

- Periodically distributing a newsletter to update residents and families about changes.

- Holding educational meetings with guest speakers for families and residents.

- Providing an eight-hour in-service to all employees regarding restraint reduction techniques (now part of orientation); purchasing a videotape educational series for the library.

- Holding breakfast educational sessions for physicians.

- Providing one-on-one training through observational methods.

### Review

The three _____ _____ selected to monitor changes resulting from improvement efforts were used to assess whether the planned improvements were bringing the desired outcomes.

**performance measures**

## Module 3: Performance Measure Calculations

Performance measures can be calculated (constructed) in different ways. The user of the information (data) should understand what is being measured and how. Also, the statistical analysis of the data can be influenced by how the measure is calculated. Three common measure constructs are measures calculated as proportions, ratios, and means, as shown by the following equations:

*Proportion* (often called "rate" or "percentage rate" if multiplied by 100):
Fall rate = (number of residents who had 1 or more falls) ÷ (number of residents)

*Ratio* of two different but related things:
Falls per 100 resident days = (number of falls) ÷ (sum of all resident days) x 100

*Mean*, or simple mathematical average (continuous data):
Average number of falls per resident = (number of falls) ÷ (number of residents)

*Note:* The pros and cons of different measure constructs can be widely debated. Generally, more statistically robust analyses can be performed using continuous data. For example, the number of prescribed medications per resident is more robust, statistically speaking, than the percentage (rate) of residents who have more than nine medications prescribed. Ratio measures can add a degree of risk adjustment, in that patients who have central lines in place longer may be more likely to develop primary bloodstream infections. Performance measurement using proportion (rate) data has been widely used in health care.

*Review*

- Performance measures such as mortality rates, infection rates, pressure ulcer rates, and bed occupancy rates are calculated as _____ data. **proportion (rate)**

- Performance measures for infection control, such as those used in the National Nosocomial Infection System (NNIS) for hospitals from the Centers for Disease Control and Prevention (CDC) include the number of primary bloodstream infections per 1,000 central line days, and the number of ventilator-related pneumonia episodes per 1,000 ventilator days. These are examples of _____ data. **ratio**

- Performance measures used to report the average length of stay or average cost are examples of continuous variable data that are reported as a _____ measurement value. **mean (average)**

## Module 4: Calculating Rate of Restraint Use

The measurement data in Table A—1 (below) can be displayed in different formats, including

- rows and columns (a table);

- a bar chart;

- a line graph;

- a run chart; and

- a control chart.

Figures A–2 through A–4 (pages 145–146) depict a bar chart and simple line graphs for the same data. Graphical displays are considered helpful in understanding and interpreting data and are well suited for presentation purposes. However, a few guidelines should be considered. When using vertical bar charts, three-dimensional charts should be avoided because they tend to visually distort the rates, making interpretation more difficult for the user. In line graphs, the addition of multiple lines representing related measures will give a more detailed picture of the overall results or findings. When two measures are highly correlated to one another, it may be helpful and informative to display both together (see Figure A–4). In the case of SLV's three performance measures, the third measure, falls with injury, also relates closely to the other two measures; however, the addition of another line might make the chart appear cluttered. This decision becomes one of preference for the chart's creator and users.

**Table A–1. Rate of Restraint Use for Given Time Periods**

| Time Period | Numerator (No. of Residents Restrained) | Denominator (All Residents) | Rate (Numerator ÷ Denominator) |
|---|---|---|---|
| 1 | 120 | 185 | 0.65 |
| 2 | 109 | 182 | 0.60 |
| 3 | 91 | 190 | 0.48 |
| 4 | 68 | 195 | 0.35 |
| 5 | 35 | 193 | 0.18 |
| 6 | 30 | 200 | 0.15 |
| 7 | 18 | 198 | 0.09 |
| 8 | 10 | 197 | 0.05 |
| 9 | 5 | 198 | 0.03 |
| 10 | 0 | 201 | 0.00 |
| 11 | 0 | 202 | 0.00 |
| 12 | 0 | 203 | 0.00 |

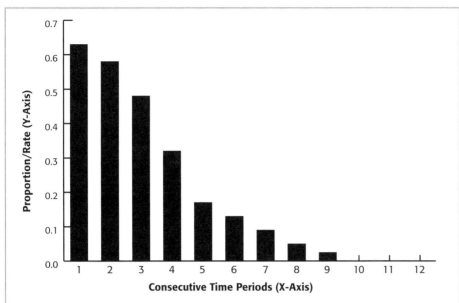

**Figure A–2. Vertical Bar Chart for Rate of Restraint Use**

This bar chart uses the same data presented in Table A–1, but the downward trend is more readily apparent.

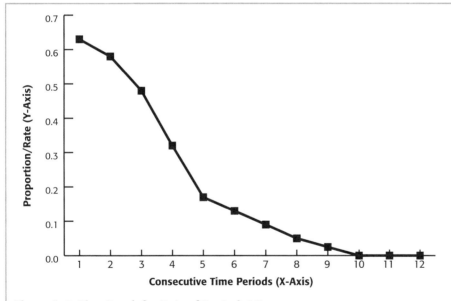

**Figure A–3. Line Graph for Rate of Restraint Use**

The decrease in restraint use is shown even more clearly in this line graph than in Figure A–2 . Again, the same data from Table A–1 are used.

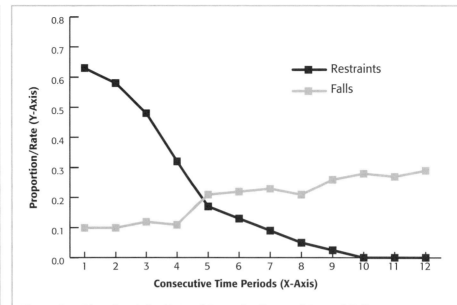

**Figure A–4. Line Graph for Rate of Restraint Use and Rate of Falls**
Because these two measures are so closely related, it is helpful to look at their findings together. According to this line graph, there is an inverse correlation in the rate of restraint use and the rate of falls.

*Review*

Just by looking at the data in Table A–1, it is possible to see that SLV's observed rate of restraint use is _____ **decreasing** each time period. This _____ trend in performance **downward** indicates that the facility has met its target level of performance on this measure.

## Module 5: Run Charts

Run charts can be used with any type of data to get a quick look at the data and interpret them using the three run chart tests for special cause variation described in Chapter 4 (page 66). The only calculation necessary for the run chart is limited to determining the facility's observed rate for each data point. Data points must be consecutively time-ordered, and a minimum of 10 to 12 data points are required. The data may be gathered weekly, monthly, bimonthly, quarterly, semiannually, or annually—whichever is best, based on the need for timely analysis and to have a sufficient number of cases (usually 10 or more) in each data point.

The run chart in Figure A–5 (below) is based on the data in Table A–2 (page 148). The rates are sorted from lowest to highest, and the two middle numbers are averaged (added together and divided by 2) to find the median. In this case, 0.17 (Time Period 4) and 0.15 (Time Period 7) are the middle numbers. The median is thus 0.16 by calculating (0.17 + 0.15) ÷ 2 = 0.16. The median can also be found by sliding a piece of paper down from the top of the graph until half the data points (five for this data set) are visible and drawing a horizontal line across the graph (see Figure 4–9, page 67).

*Note:* For an odd number of data points, such as 11, the middle point (point number 6) would be the median.

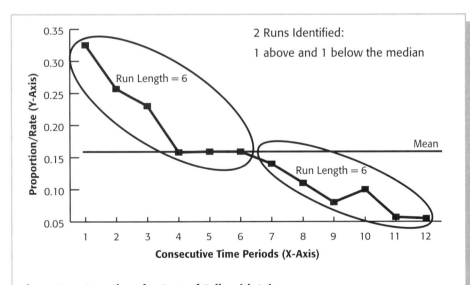

**Figure A–5. Run Chart for Rate of Falls with Injury**

Two separate runs are identified in this chart—one above and one below the median, which is calculated at 0.16.

**Table A–2. Rate of Falls with Injuries**

| Time Period | Observed Rate of Falls (Proportion) |
|---|---|
| 1 | 0.33 |
| 2 | 0.30 |
| 3 | 0.25 |
| 4 | 0.17 |
| 5 | 0.18 |
| 6 | 0.18 |
| 7 | 0.15 |
| 8 | 0.12 |
| 9 | 0.10 |
| 10 | 0.12 |
| 11 | 0.09 |
| 12 | 0.08 |

*Review*

Using Chapter 4's run chart tests for 12 data points, list the two tests that are positive for the run chart in Figure A–5:

**maximum run length**

**number of runs**

_____ _____ _____ = 6 (expected to be 5)

_____ ___ _____ = 2 (expected to be between 3 and 10)

*Note:* Variation due to a special cause (performance improvement plan) exists. Because of the decreasing number of falls with injury, the plan appears to be successful.

## Module 6: Types of Control Charts

Sometimes a run chart is all that is needed to interpret whether a problem exists or whether a planned improvement is successful. Other times (especially if only common cause variation is found in the run chart), a more sophisticated control chart is needed to identify whether special cause variation exists (that is, whether the process is out of statistical control).

*Note:* Special cause variation is important to identify problematic areas needing further investigation and to determine whether a planned improvement is working. To review the control chart tests for special cause variation, see Chapter 5 (page 95).

There are many different types of control charts. For the type of performance measurement data often used in health care, the following control charts are usually sufficient:

| | |
|---|---|
| p-chart | For proportion data (such as prevalence of weight loss and mortality rates) |
| u-chart | For ratio data (such as units of 100 or 1,000 days and number of infections per 1,000 line days) |
| X-bar S chart | A paired control chart for continuous variable data (such as average cost) |
| XmR chart | A paired control chart for continuous variable data for an individual (such as a single resident's daily weight) |

As a general rule, a minimum average number of cases (five to ten) per data point should exist for both the p-chart and the u-chart. Otherwise, special statistical techniques are used to calculate more generous upper and lower control limits for small sample sizes. A minimum average of ten cases per data point is suggested for the X-bar S chart. The Joint Commission uses the XmR chart when the average number of cases is less than ten for continuous variable data, thereby treating each data point as a single case.

The control chart in Figure A–6 (page 150) for the rate of falls measure has straight upper and lower control limit lines. This is because the number of residents changes little from time period to time period. Some control charts will have uneven, or "stair-step," upper and lower control limits (Figure A–7, page 150), because the standard deviation is recalculated for each time period and is influenced by the number of residents.

The upper control limit line in Figure A–7 is further from the mean or center line when fewer cases (residents) exist as compared to other months (September 1999 and January, February, May, and June 2000). The opposite is true when there are more cases for a month; then the month's control limit lines are closer. The lower control limit line does not show; this is because it calculates to negative numbers. Because this is a proportion measure, the observed data must be between zero and one, by definition. Therefore, the lower control limit is artificially set at zero.

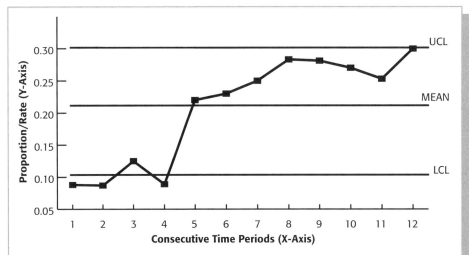

**Figure A–6. Control Chart for Rate of Falls—p-chart**
Because the number of residents in the measure's denominator stays roughly the same for each time period, the upper and lower control limits are straight lines.

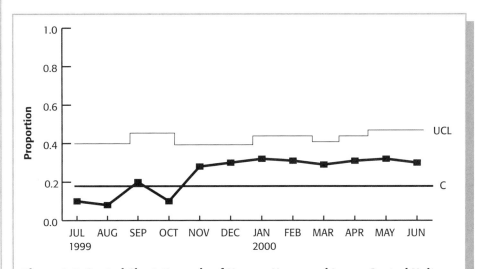

**Figure A–7. Control Chart: Example of Uneven Upper and Lower Control Units**
Because the number of residents in the measure's denominator changes for each time period, the upper and lower control limits are uneven, resembling stair steps.

*Review*

Statistical tests for _____ _____   **special cause**
variation include

- any point beyond the upper or lower control limit;

- a run of eight data points on one side of the mean; and

- six consecutive data points that steadily
  _____ or _____.   **increase,**
                                            **decrease**

Is it true or false that an "observed rate" data point falling
exactly on the upper control limit is considered to be out of   **false**
statistical control? _____

Because all three performance measures used by SLV for its
restraint reduction initiative are proportion measures, the
control chart of choice is most likely the _____ —if   **p-chart**
the average sample size (per data point) is sufficient for this
type of statistical analysis.

The number of denominator cases per each data point (average sample size) for both the restraint use measure and the
fall rate measure are the same—the number of residents.
However, the denominator is different for the fall injury rate
measure because it looks only at those residents who experienced a _____; then, the numerator represents those   **fall**
who fell and also suffered an injury. Therefore, the denominator for the fall injury rate is equal to the _____ of   **numerator**
the fall rate measure.

## Module 7: Developing Control Charts

To develop a control chart, the overall process mean for the performance measure must first be calculated, as shown in Table A–3 (below) for SLV's rate of falls measure.

**Table A–3. Rate of Falls**

| Time Period | Numerator (Number of Falls) | Denominator (All Residents) | Rate (Numerator ÷ Denominator) |
|---|---|---|---|
| 1 | 18 | 185 | 0.10 |
| 2 | 16 | 182 | 0.09 |
| 3 | 27 | 190 | 0.20 |
| 4 | 21 | 195 | 0.11 |
| 5 | 42 | 193 | 0.22 |
| 6 | 48 | 200 | 0.24 |
| 7 | 51 | 198 | 0.26 |
| 8 | 45 | 197 | 0.23 |
| 9 | 55 | 198 | 0.28 |
| 10 | 58 | 201 | 0.29 |
| 11 | 54 | 202 | 0.27 |
| 12 | 61 | 203 | 0.30 |
| Summary data | 496 | 2,344 | 496 ÷ 2,344 = .021 (mean) |

Figure A–8 (page 153) was drawn and a mean calculated based on these data. Although the actual mean is 0.2116041, it is rounded to 0.21.

*Note:* Differences in rounding for decimal places at intermediary calculation steps can cause slightly different results. *This is okay.* As a rule of thumb, try to use six to eight decimal places for intermediate calculations and then round the final results to one to three decimal places for display and/or reporting purposes.

The next step is to add upper and lower control limits to identify when the measure is within and outside statistical control (that is, when it has common cause or special cause variation). The denominator (*n*) and rate for each time period are taken from Table A–3. This information is plugged into the following equation to calculate the standard deviation (SD) for each time period:

$$\sqrt{\frac{\text{Mean} \times (1 - \text{Mean})}{n}}$$

Thus, the square root of 0.21(1 – 0.21) divided by 185 equals the standard deviation of 0.0300 for time period 1.

To find the upper and lower control limits for each time period, the individual standard deviation is multiplied by 3 and added to (upper limit) or subtracted from (lower limit) the mean. Thus, the upper control limit for time period 1 is 0.21 + (3 x 0.0300) = 0.302. The lower control limit is 0.21 – (3 x 0.0300) = 0.122. Table A–4 (page 154) shows the standard deviations and upper and lower control

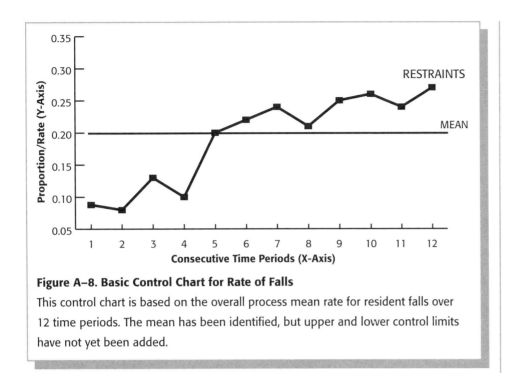

**Figure A–8. Basic Control Chart for Rate of Falls**

This control chart is based on the overall process mean rate for resident falls over 12 time periods. The mean has been identified, but upper and lower control limits have not yet been added.

limits for each time period. Figure A–9 (page 154) is the control chart from Figure A–8 with upper and lower control limits added per the data in Table A–4.

The p-chart in Figure A–9 was developed with a spreadsheet program. Spreadsheet packages are probably not the best software to use to create and interpret traditional-looking control charts, but they are often readily accessible and can be used to create valid, interpretable charts. When using spreadsheet packages, the formulas and charts have to be created manually.

To get the control chart look using spreadsheet packages, eliminate or suppress the data point marks (circles, triangles, diamonds, and so forth) for the control limits and center lines. The upper and lower control limit lines may not appear stair-shaped as in traditional control charts, but may appear as a line that has "connected the dots without the dots." The control chart can still be validly interpreted using the out-of-statistical-control tests.

**Table A–4. Calculations for Upper and Lower Control Limits for Rate of Falls**

| Time Period | Denominator (n) | Rate | Standard Deviation | Upper Control Limit | Lower Control Limit |
|---|---|---|---|---|---|
| 1 | 185 | 0.10 | 0.0300 | 0.302 | 0.122 |
| 2 | 182 | 0.09 | 0.0302 | 0.301 | 0.119 |
| 3 | 190 | 0.20 | 0.0295 | 0.299 | 0.121 |
| 4 | 195 | 0.11 | 0.0292 | 0.298 | 0.122 |
| 5 | 193 | 0.22 | 0.0293 | 0.298 | 0.122 |
| 6 | 200 | 0.24 | 0.0288 | 0.296 | 0.124 |
| 7 | 198 | 0.26 | 0.0289 | 0.297 | 0.123 |
| 8 | 197 | 0.23 | 0.0290 | 0.297 | 0.123 |
| 9 | 198 | 0.28 | 0.0289 | 0.297 | 0.123 |
| 10 | 201 | 0.29 | 0.0287 | 0.296 | 0.124 |
| 11 | 202 | 0.27 | 0.0287 | 0.296 | 0.124 |
| 12 | 203 | 0.30 | 0.0286 | 0.296 | 0.124 |

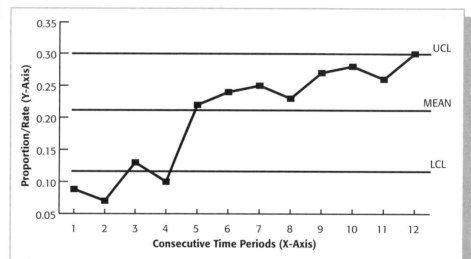

**Figure A–9. Detailed Control Chart for Rate of Falls—p-chart**

This control chart builds on Figure A–8 by identifying the upper and lower control limits for the rate of falls performance measure.

*Review*

Control charts use the overall process _____ (wheras run charts use the median) for the center line. The upper and lower control limit lines are added next.

**mean**

The overall process mean for the p-chart is calculated by summing all numerator cases and dividing that number by the sum of all denominator cases. Then, the resulting mean becomes the _____ line of the control chart.

**center**

A control chart may lack a _____ look in its upper and lower control limit lines if the number of cases in the denominator is basically the same from one time period to another.

**stair-shaped**

## Module 8: Analyzing Results

Once the data have been collected and the results calculated and displayed, the organization must decide what the results mean. As shown in Figure A–10 (below), SLV's rate of falls measure is out of statistical control. Points 1, 2, and 4 lay outside the lower control limit. Point 12 triggers the test for eight consecutive data points on one side of the mean, which indicates that a process shift (decreased use of restraints) has occurred.

Because a change in one process can affect others positively or negatively, it is a good idea to track performance measures in related areas. With the changes SLV introduced through its restraint reduction program, it also saw changes in the use of psychoactive medications (Figure A–11, page 157), employee turnover rates (Figure A–12, page 157), and the average daily census (Figure A–13, page 158).

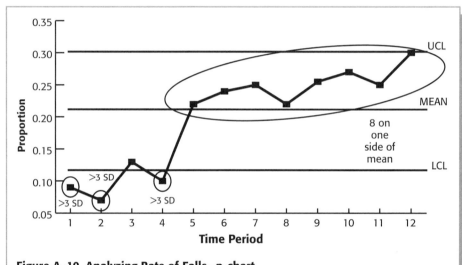

**Figure A–10. Analyzing Rate of Falls—p-chart**
The control chart from Figure A–9 is marked to show that the performance measure (rate of falls) is out of statistical control.

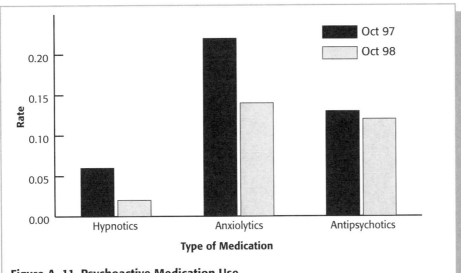

**Figure A–11. Psychoactive Medication Use**

The use of hypnotics, anxiolytics, and antipsychotics was reduced during the first year of the initiative.

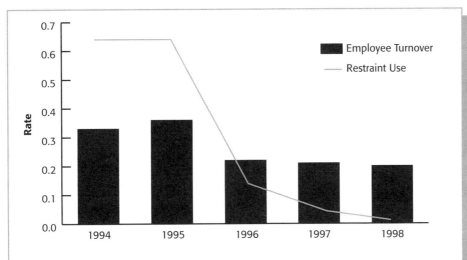

**Figure A–12. Employee Turnover Rates**

High employee turnover is a widespread problem in the long term care industry. According to data collected on this measure, SLV experienced a decrease in employee turnover after the start of the restraint reduction program.

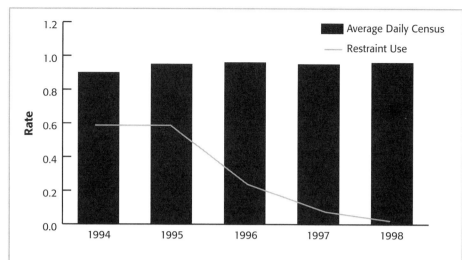

**Figure A–13. Average Daily Census**
The average daily census for SLV showed a slight increase during the restraint reduction initiative. This may reflect physicians' and hospital personnel's support of the program.

*Review*

Because of their literature review and investigational research, SLV staff expected the fall rate to increase once restraint use was reduced. They also monitored the fall injury rate. Time period 5 in Figure A–10 shows the fall rate to be increasing; however, the same period in the run chart for rate of falls with injury (see Figure A–5) shows that the fall injury rate is _____. This also was **decreasing** expected based on literature review, so SLV proceeded to remove restraints on more challenging residents.

## Conclusion

Jennifer Mowery, BSW, director of social services, and Linda Lesher, LPN, continuous quality improvement director, summarize the improvements SLV realized from moving to restraint-free care:

- A reduction in the severity of injuries related to falls;

- A decrease in the number of psychoactive medications use, with the most dramatic decrease evident in the use of hypnotics;

- A growth in resident participation in activities such as watering plants, caring for animals, and gardening;

- An improvement in staff morale related to the satisfaction of delivering high-quality care (measured by a decrease in the staff turnover rate);

- A decrease in complaints regarding care issues;

- An increase in the number of discharges to home; and

- The development of a fall analysis form to aid in early identification of the causes of falls.

SLV now serves as a training site for restraint-free care in Pennsylvania, which has legislated a statewide restraint reduction initiative with a goal to decrease restraint use to 10%. (At the end of Year 2, the restraint usage rate in Pennsylvania had decreased from 28.6% to 14%.)

## Reference

1. Thomas WH: *Life Worth Living: How Someone You Love Can Still Enjoy Life in a Nursing Home—The Eden Alternative in Action.* Acton, MA: VanderWyk and Burnham, 1996.

# Appendix B: How Joint Commission Surveyors Will Use ORYX Data

This appendix provides sample questions pertaining to performance measurement that surveyors may ask during surveys. *Note: Some standards may not apply to all settings.* The general meaning of the standard is given first, followed by a description of what surveyors will look for regarding ORYX requirements, including possible questions, where appropriate.

## Improving Organization Performance Standards

*Leaders establish a planned, systematic, organizationwide approach to process design and performance measurement, analysis, and improvement.*

The ORYX Initiative does not change the focus of the improving performance organization (PI) standards, and questions such as "How are leaders involved in the design and implementation of PI activities?" and "Are PI activities carried out in a collaborative fashion among departments and disciplines?" will continue to be asked. However, the surveyor may ask questions about how the selected ORYX measures fit into the organization's strategic approach to performance improvement, including the following:

- How do the ORYX measures reflect the patient population served?

- How were patient needs and concerns considered in the ORYX measure selection process (high-volume, high-risk, problem-prone areas)?

- How were ORYX measure selections communicated to staff?

- How are the ORYX data integrated into the organization's overall PI activities?

*New or modified processes are designed well.*

If ORYX measurement data led to a new or modified process, the surveyor may ask how appropriate improvement actions were identified and implemented, and whether improvement actions were tested first. The surveyor may also address how and which staff were involved with identification and implementation of improvement strategies at multiple administrative levels, across disciplines (clinical), and across departments.

*Data are collected to monitor the stability of existing processes, identify opportunities for improvement, and sustain improvements.*

*Appropriate statistical techniques are used to analyze and display data.*

The surveyor may ask what mechanisms were used to minimize measurement bias (such as randomization, stratification, and risk adjustment) when analyzing special causes or unsatisfactory comparisons.

The use of ORYX data in the survey process began in 2000, and the Joint Commission is interested in how health care organizations review the comparative feedback reports from their selected measurement systems. Surveyors may ask the following:

- Has the organization received comparative feedback from its performance measurement system(s)?

- Are the comparison data numerical (table or columns) or graphic (charts)?

- Is the feedback report well understood by and useful to staff?

- Are missing data points available and noted for the surveyor?

- Are data different from those transmitted to the Joint Commission? If so, why?

*Improved performance is achieved and sustained.*

The surveyor may ask staff to

- describe how performance measurement data were disseminated and displayed in the organization;

- describe the mechanisms implemented for monitoring the results of improvement actions;

- describe the organization's approach to achieving and sustaining improved performance; and

- explain whether improvement strategies have been incorporated into operating procedures and organizational policies.

## Leadership Standards

*The planning process provides for setting performance improvement priorities and identifies how the health care organization adjusts priorities in response to unusual or urgent events.*

The surveyor will be interested in what steps the health care organization has taken to select measures to meet the accreditation participation requirements related to ORYX. From the leadership point of view, how are ORYX measurement results monitored, and what actions are taken when results are not satisfactory? Additional questions will address the role leaders have taken in identifying priority areas for performance measurement and improvement, how expectations were set, and how plans were developed for managing the performance improvement process.

Leaders at board level may be questioned in regard to whether the board played a visible role in performance measurement activities.

*Organization leaders set expectations, develop plans, and manage processes to measure, assess, and improve the quality of the organization's governance, management, clinical, and support activities.*

For hospitals in particular, the surveyor may ask how the medical staff has been involved in the selection of ORYX measures and implementation of activities to assess and improve organization performance. Also, the surveyor may ask how findings have been communicated to the medical staff.

Questions relating to the organization's approach to performance measurement for ORYX may focus on organizational priorities and strategic directions, and whether the selected measures support/complement the organization's mission, vision, and strategies for improvement. Surveyors will be interested to learn how the organization's priorities for performance improvement are established and how they are linked to important organizational and patient care processes and outcomes.

## Management of the Environment of Care Standards

*A management plan addresses utility systems (including data exchange systems).*

The surveyor may ask how management has minimized the risks involved with communication systems and data exchange systems for ORYX data.

## Management of Information Standards

*Confidentiality, security, and integrity of data.*

A surveyor may question how the organization balances data sharing for comparative and performance improvement purposes while appropriately managing data confidentiality.

*Uniform data definitions and data capture methods.*

The quality of the collected data, as well as the completeness of the data, are important to their use. Surveyors may question how staff were trained in information management and the use of data analysis tools.

Because the quality of submitted data is key to their overall usefulness, questions will relate to how the organization monitors its data for accuracy and completeness to ensure that valid and reliable data are being used to make decisions.

*Decision makers and other appropriate staff are trained in the principles of information management.*

A surveyor may ask what methods were used to educate and train staff involved in generating, collecting, and validating data for ORYX measures. Additional training questions may focus on statistical tools and data analysis methods that were used to help staff transform data into relevant information.

*Timely and accurate data transmissions.*

ORYX measurement data are due to be transmitted to the Joint Commission four months after the end of each quarter—by the health care organization's selected performance measurement system(s). However, each performance measurement system has its own unique data deadline for participating organizations. It is up to the health care organization to get its data to the measurement system by that system's deadline. This deadline is often 30 to 60 days prior to the Joint Commission's transmission deadline. The measurement system needs this time to

- ensure data quality (and contact organizations regarding questionable data);

- perform statistical analyses;

- perform risk adjustment—if its measures are adjusted for patients' severity factors;

- format the measurement data as detailed in the Joint Commission's *ORYX Technical Implementation Guide* for performance measurement systems; and

- transmit the data electronically to the Joint Commission in a special electronic data interchange (EDI) file.

Because credible statistical analysis depends on accurate and complete data transmissions, surveyors may question what happened if an organization's selected measure(s) has missing monthly data points. In particular, what happened and what was done to prevent this from happening again?

The health care organization will not receive a lower score due to errors or problems originating with the performance measurement system.

*External databases.*

The ORYX initiative makes an organization compliant with this standard. The surveyor may ask for a description of the comparison group (external database) for selected measures.

## Surveillance, Prevention, and Control of Infection Standards

*The infection control process is designed to lower the risks and to improve the (proportional) rates or (numerical) trends of epidemiologically significant infections.*

If the health care organization has selected an infection control measure, that data may guide the surveyor to ask how it is using the resulting data to improve the quality of care delivered to the patient.

# Suggested Readings

The following books and journal articles provide more in-depth information about statistical process control, including the use of comparison charts and analysis. Readers may also wish to refer to available textbooks for help with basic statistical analysis.

## Books

### General

- Carey RG, Lloyd RC: *Measuring Quality Improvement in Healthcare: A Guide to Statistical Process Control Applications*. New York: Quality Resources, 1995.

- Gitlow H, et al: *Tools and Methods for the Improvement of Quality*, Homewood, IL: Irwin, 1989.

- Grant E, Leavenworth R: *Statistical Quality Control*, 7th ed. New York: John Wiley & Sons, 1996.

- Kirk R: *Managing Outcomes, Process, and Cost in a Managed Care Environment*. Gaithersburg, MD: Aspen Publishers, Inc, 1997.

- Montgomery D: *Introduction to Statistical Quality Control*, 3rd ed. New York: John Wiley & Sons, 1996.

- Pitt H: *SPC For the Rest of Us: A Personal Path to Statistical Process Control*. Reading, MA: Addison-Wesley, 1994.

- Pyzdek T: *Pyzdek's Guide to SPC, Volume I: Fundamentals*. Tucson, AZ: Quality Publishing, LLC, 1998.

- Wheeler DJ, Chambers DS: *Understanding Statistical Process Control*. Knoxville, TN: SPC Press, Inc, 1992.

### Use of Comparison Charts

- Shwartz M, Ash AS, Iezzoni LI: Comparing outcomes across providers. In *Risk Adjustment for Measuring Outcomes*. Chicago: Health Administration Press, 1997, pp 472–516.

- Wassertheil-Smoller S: *Biostatistics and Epidemiology: A Primer for Health Professionals*. New York: Springer-Verlag, 1995.

## Journal Articles

### Statistical Process Control in Health Care

- Balestracci D Jr, Barlow JL: *Quality Improvement: Practical Applications for Medical Group Practice*, 2nd ed. Englewood, CO: Center for Research in Ambulatory Health Care Administration, 1996.

- Boggs PB, et al: Using statistical process control charts for the continual improvement of asthma care. *The Joint Commission Journal on Quality Improvement* 25:163–181, 1999.

- Carey RG, Teeters JL: CQI case study: Reducing medication errors. *The Joint Commission Journal on Quality Improvement* 21:232–237, 1995.

- Carlin E, Carlson R, Nordin J: Using continuous quality improvement tools to improve pediatric immunization rates. *The Joint Commission Journal on Quality Improvement* 22:277–288, 1996.

- Finison LJ, Finison KS, Bliersbach CM: The use of control charts to improve healthcare quality. *Journal for Healthcare Quality* 15(1):9–23, 1993.

- Levett J, Carey RG: Measuring for improvement: From Toyota to thoracic surgery. *Annals of Thoracic Surgery* 68:353–358, 1999.

- Mitchell L, et al: Three teams improving thrombolytic therapy. *The Joint Commission Journal on Quality Improvement* 22:379–390, 1996.

- Nugent W, et al: Designing an instrument panel to monitor and improve coronary artery bypass grafting. *Journal of Clinical Outcomes Management* 1(2):57–64, 1994.

- Ornstein SM, et al: The computer-based patient record as a CQI tool in a family medicine center. *The Joint Commission Journal on Quality Improvement* 23:347–361, 1997.

- Page US, Washburn T: Using tracking data to find complications that physicians miss: The case of renal failure in cardiac surgery. *The Joint Commission Journal on Quality Improvement* 23:511–520, 1997.

- Pyzdek T: Preventing hospital falls. *Quality Digest* 19(5):26–27, 1999.

- Pyzdek T: Variation and your health. *Quality Digest* 18(8):22, 1998.

- Shahian DM, et al: Applications of statistical quality control to cardiac surgery. *Annals of Thoracic Surgery* 62:1353–1359, 1996.

- Solberg LI, Mosser G, McDonald S: The three faces of performance measurement: Improvement, accountability, and research. *The Joint Commission Journal on Quality Improvement* 23:135–147, 1997.

### *Use of Comparison Charts*

- Agresti A, Coull BA: Approximate is better than "exact" for interval estimation of binomial proportions. *The American Statistician* 52:119–126, 1998.

- Holubkov R, et al: Analysis, assessment, and presentation of risk-adjusted statewide obstetrical care data: The StORQS II study in Washington State. Part I. *Health Services Research* 33:531–548, 1998.

# Index

*f=figure*
*t=table*

**T**

**U**

**V**